·BE YOUR OWN FOOTBALL HERO·

RONALDO

First published in the UK in 2020 by Dino Books,
an imprint of Bonnier Books UK,
The Plaza, 535 King's Road, London SW10 0SZ
Owned by Bonnier Books,
Sveavägen 56, Stockholm, Sweden

@dinobooks
@footieheroesbks
heroesfootball.com
www.bonnierbooks.co.uk

Design by www.envydesign.co.uk

ISBN: 9781789462364

British Library Cataloguing-in-Publication Data:

A catalogue record for this book is available from the British Library.

Printed and bound in Great Britain by Clays Ltd, Elcograf S.p.A.

1 3 5 7 9 10 8 6 4 2

MATT AND TOM OLDFIELD

ULTIMATE FOOTBALL HEROES

BE YOUR OWN FOOTBALL HERO

RONALDO

FROM THE PLAYGROUND
TO THE PITCH

For all readers, young and old(er)

Dear Reader,

Welcome to a new Ultimate Football Heroes adventure…with a twist. We hope you're excited because for the first time ever, we're giving you the chance to be your own football hero!

As we take you through the amazing life story of Cristiano Ronaldo, you'll have decisions to make along the way. Do you train really hard or skip practice to hang out with your mates in the park? Do you leave Portugal behind to follow your big football dream or stay at home with your family and friends?

Depending on each option you choose, your football career will take a different direction. Will you follow the path all the way to Champions League triumph, or will you take one of the other, fictional journeys? There's only one way to find out! So, are you ready to BE YOUR OWN FOOTBALL HERO? Put your boots on because it's time for kick off…

From the moment you can walk, there's a football at your feet. Actually, it doesn't even have to be a proper football; those can often be hard to find in the poorer parts of Funchal, Madeira where you live. No, all you need is anything round that you can kick. A stone, or a piece of fruit will do, but a real football is perfect.

With one of those, you spend hours practising your skills – right foot, left foot, passing, shooting, trick after trick after trick – until you've mastered everything that you watched the bigger boys do and more.

'Cristiano!... CRISTIANO!'

You know that there'll be trouble when your sister Katia finds out and tells your mum that you've escaped without doing your homework first, but you'll worry about that later. For now, it's all about you and the football. With one of those, you spend hours playing in the street against your friends, from the end of school until darkness and dinner. You play with rocks for goalposts and the sights and sounds of city life are all around you.

'There's a car coming!' one of your teammates shouts.

The game is paused for a moment, but nothing is going to stop you from showing off those silky skills of yours. And nothing is going to stop you from getting that glory. Even at the age of six, you're already the most competitive kid in Funchal. Defeat just isn't an option. It might just be a fun game of street football to some – but not to you. To you, it's totally serious, and so you have to win, no matter what it takes – fouls, arguments, even injuries and tears. But most of the time, your talent is more than enough to overcome your opponents.

As you dribble forward, your legs are a blur of fast movements, and yet the ball stays glued to your boot. Right or left? The defender doesn't know which way you'll go because you're so good with both feet. With a stepover to the left and a burst of speed, you power your way past the first tackle and then use your skill to skip past another two challenges. The next part's easy:

Gooooooooooooooooooaaaaaaaaaaaaaaaallllllllllll lllllllllllllll!!!!!!!!!!!!!!!!!!

You celebrate like the superstar that one day

you're so determined to become. The early signs are good. Your mum named you after Ronald Reagan, a very successful man who became President of the United States of America. And then there's what the doctor said when you were born, the story that your dad never tires of telling you:

'You were a very heavy baby and as he held you in his arms, he turned to us and smiled, "Weighing that much, this boy could be a footballer!"'

Your parents have high hopes for you and encourage you to follow your dream. It helps that they're both football mad, although no-one is as football mad as you.

You know that it won't be easy to become a top professional player, but at the same time, you believe that, with hard work and your special talent, anything is possible. As a professional footballer, you would be able to do what you love and help lift your family out of poverty. Although the six of you have now moved into your own house, it's still hard with so many hungry mouths to feed. Your oldest brother and sister, Elma and Hugo, are already working to earn money for the family. This could be your way to do the same.

But wait, one step at a time! So far, you've only played street football with your friends and entertained the locals with your tricks. You haven't even played for a proper team! Yet.

For your eighth birthday, your godfather, Fernando, finally gives you the gift you've always wanted – a real football of your own.

'Wow, thanks!' you say, the smile spreading across your face until it can't stretch any further. Now all you need is an opportunity to really show what you can do with it.

When your older cousin, Nuno, comes over and sees you running rings around everyone in the street, he has an excellent idea: 'You're way too good to be playing with those guys. I'm playing at Andorinha now – you should come to training with me!'

'Cool, that would be awesome!' you reply. This is the chance that you've been hoping for, but you need to check with your dad first. Luckily for you, he thinks it's a great idea. 'Yes, it's time for you to start

playing proper football.'

Right, what are you waiting for? It feels like weeks but finally, the day of your first training session arrives. And even though Nuno has told you lots about it, you're still not prepared for what you see at Andorinha. It's so different from the street football that you're used to! The pitch is nice and flat, and there isn't a single can or bottle in sight. The only cars around are safely parked a long way away from the pitch. Plus, all the players are wearing the same light blue team shirt. Hopefully, if you play well, you'll get one of those too.

'Welcome to our club!' the coach says to you cheerfully, once he's put out all the cones for the passing and dribbling exercises.

Woah, everything seems so... professional! There's no need to get nervous, though; you're here to play football, your favourite thing in the world. You might not have much tactical knowledge yet, but you can learn that side of the game. What matters most is talent and you've got lots and lots of that.

You do well in the training drills, especially the

dribbling part. Your legs are a blur of fast movements as you dance through the cones, and yet the ball always stays glued to your boot. You make it look so easy.

'Excellent, Cristiano!' the coach claps and cheers. He's impressed, but he's seen plenty of skilful players before. Now he wants to see what you can do in an actual match.

And so do you. From what you've seen of the other Andorinha players so far, they're a talented team but there's nothing for you to fear. You just need to get on the ball, try out your full range of tricks and…

CRUNCHING TACKLE!

'Hey!' you cry out as you fly through the air before falling onto the grass. But it's no use complaining because the game is carrying on without you. Besides, it wasn't a foul; it's just that the other players are bigger and stronger and older than you.

Nuno looks over to check that you're okay. Although you're really frustrated, you manage a nod as you get back up and play on. You're not going to

let a bit of pain stop you. You chase back to try and win the ball, but it's no use because Andorinha's other players are a lot better than you thought they'd be. One-two, one-two – they pass it around you like you're the piggy in the middle.

Gooooooooooooooooooaaaaaaaaaaaaaaaallllllllllll llllllllllllllll!!!!!!!!!!!!!!!!!!!!

Oh dear, your team is 1–0 down already and it's all your fault. Maybe you're not the greatest footballer in the world, after all. Not yet anyway. Still, if you can just get your skills right, you'll be able to escape with the ball before they've even…

BANG!

WHACK!

THUD!

Wow, it's only a practice match, but the football is so fast and competitive. By the time that first Andorinha training session ends, you've got more cuts and bruises than goals and assists.

'Unlucky, kid,' the coach says as you trudge slowly off the field.

It's a disappointing start to your life in a football

team. It turns out that you've still got lots to learn. When you get home, tired and aching, your dad asks you, 'So, did you enjoy it?'

DECISION TIME

Do you say:

a) 'No, it was horrible, I hated it and I don't want to go back there!'

or

b) 'Yes, it was hard work, but I want to go back and try again!'

For a), go to page 15
For b), go to page 42

Your dad sees the sad look on your face and offers you a comforting smile. He knows how much football means to you. 'I understand, son. Don't worry, why don't you try playing with kids your own age instead?'

At first, you just give a small, sad nod but the more you think about your dad's idea, the better it sounds. Yes, that would be so much better! Against boys the same size as you, you'll be able to show off all your silky skills without being pushed and kicked around the pitch. You'll be a superstar straight away.

It takes a few weeks, but your dad does eventually find an Under-9s team for you to join. Brilliant! You can't wait to get started. As you arrive at the training ground, you notice that it's not as nice as Andorinha's, but hey, you can't have everything, can you? What matters most is that you're getting a second chance to play your favourite sport – football.

'Let's do this!' you tell yourself, feeling determined and excited.

After a quick 'Good luck!' from your dad, you walk out onto the field to meet your new teammates.

They all seem very nice and friendly, but most importantly, are they any good at football? There's only one way to find out.

You ace all of the training drills, just like you did at Andorinha. You can tell that everyone's really impressed and at first, that makes you feel good. But before long you realise that you're a lot faster, smarter and more skilful than the others – you're the best player there by far!

'Well done, Cristiano!' the coach encourages you, but everything is way too easy. For you, football is all about the battle to be the best – so where's the challenge, where's your competition?

The training session ends with a seven-a-side match, which should be your time to truly shine. But how are you supposed to do that when your teammates can't even get a simple pass right?

'Over here!' you keep calling out, but the ball never arrives. Instead, your opponents are 3–0 up already and another boy is getting all the glory.

'Great strike, Sergio!'

No way – when it comes to football, you're far too

competitive to just sit back and let your team lose like that. As you grow more and more frustrated, you think to yourself, 'How are we going to win this game? I guess I'll have to do it on my own!' So the next time your side has the ball, you steal it straight off your teammate's foot and dribble past one defender, then another, then another…

Gooooooooooooooooooaaaaaaaaaaaaaaaalllllllllllll llllllllllllll!!!!!!!!!!!!!!!!!!!

What a worldie! When you score a second and then a third solo goal to tie the game, you expect your coach to clap and cheer. But instead, he just calls out to you, 'Come on, Cristiano – stop hogging that ball. Football is a team game!'

You know that, of course, but why would you pass when the other players aren't at your level? As the session ends and you walk off the pitch, you're not sure if you want to return.

DECISION TIME

Do you:

a) Decide that team sports just aren't for you? You're an individual.

or

b) Listen to the coach and try to become a better team player?

For a), go to page 19
For b), go to page 35

Without a proper club to play for, you go back to starring in street football against your friends. And now that you've decided that you prefer being an individual, rather than a team player, you work harder than ever on your skills. That's the part you find most fun, anyway!

You spend hours watching the older boys in your neighbourhood compete to see who can do the best trick. You memorise every movement so that you don't forget, and then you go home and practise them until you're even better. Once you're feeling confident, it's time for you to show off your new skills, in front of an audience.

'Woah, did you see that?' you hear the locals saying to each other when you pull off another moment of magic. 'That kid's incredible – what an entertainer!'

More and more people start turning up to watch you perform your wizardry in the street. They're not interested in how many goals you score, or whether your team wins; no, they just want to watch your fancy flicks and tricks.

Olé!

Olé!

'Seriously, you should do your own skills show,' one of your biggest fans suggests. 'I'd pay to see that!'

Really? It's an interesting idea that's definitely worth thinking about. In the end, you decide – why not? Surely, it's worth a go! You start off with one show per week, but the crowds just get bigger and bigger. It turns out that your performances are so popular that you can fill the street every single night. It's the perfect job – you're enjoying yourself, and at the same time, you're making lots of money to help feed your family.

'Wow, I want to do this FOREVER!' you think to yourself as you listen to the crowd chanting your name.

Cristiano! Cristiano! Cristiano!

For you, aged eight, it's the greatest feeling in the world and you never want it to end.

DECISION TIME

Do you:

a) Eventually get tired of doing the same old tricks and decide to try something else?

or

b) Stick with your skills shows, getting better and better?

For a), go to page 23
For b), go to page 22

Football and entertainment – what a winning combination! Congratulations, you've found your perfect job and those street performances in Madeira are just the start for you. Word spreads about your super skills and soon, someone introduces you to the world of freestyle competitions. You're hooked, and once you've perfected your routine, you go on to become the local champion. After that, it's time to go and try your luck in Lisbon, Portugal's capital city. There are lots of talented freestylers there, but with lots of hard work and dedication, you make a name for yourself. And from there, your tricks and flicks take you all across Europe and even to America.

Your cool videos get millions of views, turning you into a social media star. Everyone wants to know how you learned your magical moves. So while you might not be the Cristiano Ronaldo we know and love today, getting all the fame and glory on the football pitch, you still get to travel the world and show off your fancy skills as a famous freestyle footballer.

THE END

Right, what other fun things are there to do in Funchal? At first, without your football tricks to practise, you're feeling pretty lost. How are you going to fill all those free hours after school and at the weekend?

'Why don't you try playing another sport?' your cousin Nuno suggests one day when he sees you looking really fed up. 'How about tennis? I reckon you'll like it because you get to be a one-man team!'

At first, you're not too sure – you're super skilful with your feet, but your hands? You don't know; you've never really tried. What if you're terrible at tennis and it turns out to be an embarrassing experience? You hate losing, remember!

Also, how and where will you play? Tennis isn't as easy as football; you need equipment and space to play. Your family doesn't have enough money to buy you a racquet and most of the tennis courts in Madeira are near the hotels in the tourist area. There's no way that they're going to welcome in two boys from Funchal.

'Don't worry, Cristiano – I've got it sorted!' Nuno has two old racquets and he knows somewhere to play, so you can't say no. Besides, what's the worst that can happen?

'Right, let's start slow,' Nuno says, sounding like your coach.

At first, the racquet feels a bit strange in your hands as you move around the court. And once you've got used to it, the idea of hitting a small ball back and forth begins to feel a bit boring. But when you try to up the pace and power, your shots keep landing long or wide.

'OUT!' Nuno calls again and again.

'Arggh, I hate this game!' you scream in frustration, throwing your racquet at the ground.

But now that you've decided to give tennis a try, you're determined to improve your accuracy. You're the most competitive kid in Funchal, after all. An hour of hard hitting and relentless rallies later, you collapse on to the clay, covered in sweat.

'Well played!' Nuno gasps in between breaths.

Although he is the winner, you've given him his toughest test in ages. He's really impressed with your talent.

'Hey, you're not bad for a beginner!' your cousin says, and you beam with pride.

'Same time tomorrow?' you ask.

DECISION TIME

Do you:

a) Decide that, actually, tennis is too boring for you. Where are the chances to show off your skills? No, that's it; you've lost your passion for sports. It's time for something new.

or

b) Decide that tennis is definitely going to be your new thing. Nuno's right; you're not bad for a beginner and you're determined to keep working until you become the best player in Funchal.

For a), go to page 28
For b), go to page 26

Right, if you're going to become the best tennis player in Funchal, you've got lots of work to do. Day after day, you practise to perfect your full range of shots – serves, volleys, smashes, forehand, backhand – until eventually, you're thrashing Nuno every time. And that's when a local coach spots your promising potential.

'You're good, kid,' he tells you, 'and with some guidance from me, you could be great. What do you think – would you like me to come and train at my academy?'

You nod eagerly. 'Yes please!'

Congratulations, you're on your way to becoming a top tennis star! The first step is becoming the Champion of Madeira. Once you achieve that at the age of nineteen, your coach starts entering you into national tournaments in Porto, Lisbon, and Braga. You're hardly ever at home in Funchal anymore. The money is pretty good as long as you win, and you win more and more matches as you move up the tennis ladder – first to the Futures tournaments, then the ATP Challenger Tour, until at last you're playing

on the ATP tour against the likes of Rafael Nadal, Roger Federer and Andy Murray. Although you never quite reach their amazing level, you still enjoy a good career in your second sport.

THE END

So far, your life has been all about sports, but there are lots of other hobbies out there. Your godfather, Fernando, knows that you've fallen out of love with football, so for your ninth birthday, he gives you a different kind of gift.

'What's this?' you think to yourself as you excitedly tear off the wrapping paper.

It's... a guitar. 'Cool, thanks!' you say politely but when you hold it in your hands, you realise you have no idea how to play it. After staring at the strings for a while, you try plucking one of them. *Twang!* No, that sounds horrible!

'Don't worry, Cristiano,' Fernando laughs when he sees your shocked face. 'It's not as hard as it looks! I'll teach you how to play.'

Every week, your godfather comes over to give you a lesson, and in between, you practise and practise the songs that he shows you. From first thing in the morning until last thing at night, the sound of your guitar fills the family home.

'Well done, you're getting good at that,' your mum encourages you.

'Yes, thank goodness – if I heard much more of that rusty gate screech, I think I'd go mad!' your dad jokes, but you can tell that he's proud of you really.

Just like with your football tricks, once you've mastered a few songs on the guitar, you want to show them off. You were born to entertain. You start by performing at a few family parties, and when that goes well, you try performing out in the street, in that same spot where you used to put on your skills shows. Although it's a different talent, you get the same reaction:

'Bravo!' your audience claps and cheers. 'More, more!'

When the locals request new songs, you learn them and add them to your setlist, until you could play for them all night long.

'One more song! One more song!'

After taking a bow, you walk home with a happy feeling and a heavy guitar case from all the money that you've collected. You love playing guitar and entertaining a crowd, but is this something that you want to do forever?

DECISION TIME

Do you:

a) Take your guitar skills to the next level by forming a band with some of your friends?

or

b) Keep playing your guitar, but only for fun – as a hobby rather than a career?

For a), go to page 31
For b), go to page 33

At first, the band is just for fun. You did it because you enjoy hanging out with your friends and playing music together. But the more you practise, the better you sound. 'Could we make it big?' you begin to wonder. From playing covers of old songs, you move on to writing ones of your own. It's so exciting and you're eager to see what other people think of them.

'I think it's time for us to perform at a concert,' you suggest one day, and the others all agree.

You start out in a small local bar but soon, you're playing at the biggest clubs in Madeira. What a feeling! Suddenly, you're a local celebrity and everyone knows your band's name, plus the words to all your biggest hits. What next? Playing gigs in Portugal's biggest cities, Porto and Lisbon, and then in Spain and France too. Why not? You dare to dream big. Congratulations, you're ready to become a rock star.

You and your bandmates move to Lisbon and play gig after gig, until eventually a record company spots your potential. Your first album is a huge success all across Europe and you even get to tour South America.

You might not have made it as a football superstar, but you're the guitarist in a successful rock band, and so you still get to play in front of big crowds every night.

THE END

Although you have many talents, maybe you don't need to be the best at everything, after all. Wouldn't it be more fun to have lots of different interests at the same time – football, freestyle, tennis, guitar – instead of only one serious obsession? When you stop putting so much pressure on yourself to succeed, you start to feel happier.

'You've changed,' your friends tease you during your street football games. 'What happened to that super competitive kid we used to know?'

You shrug and smile cheekily. 'I might not want to win as much as I used to but watch out, because I can still beat you guys any day of the week!'

Congratulations, you're doing what feels right for you. Who needs a famous football career? You're too busy having different kinds of fun every night of the week, and meeting lots of new people. Life feels exciting and you're really enjoying yourself. When one of your musician friends tells you about a job at one of Madeira's fanciest restaurants, you decide to add 'chef' to your long list of talents. You work your way up from the bottom until you become the best in Madeira. When a wealthy customer recommends you to one of his friends, you're offered the chance to work in a restaurant on a cruise ship. You get to cook delicious food, plus play a bit of guitar and tennis in your free time, while travelling the world in style.

THE END

At first, you find it difficult to trust your new teammates, but as the weeks go by, it does start to get easier. When you see the space open up in front of you on the football pitch, ZOOM! you're off, using your skill and speed to dribble past defender after defender, until…

Gooooooooooooooooooaaaaaaaaaaaaaaaallllllllllll llllllllllllll!!!!!!!!!!!!!!!!!!

Sometimes, however, when you try to twist and turn your way out of a tackle, you just can't escape. Before, you would have kept going until you lost the ball, but now you look up and see your fellow attacker is in lots of space, in a great position to score.

Gooooooooooooooooooaaaaaaaaaaaaaaaallllllllllll llllllllllllll!!!!!!!!!!!!!!!!!!

'That's it – great pass, Cristiano!' your coach encourages you.

'Thanks for the assist!' your fellow attacker cheers, giving you a high-five.

It feels good to share the glory and you're making lots of new friends. You're still the star player, but you're also a team player, and together, you're

winning game after game after game.

'If we keep this up, we could win the league!' you declare confidently.

Yes, on the football pitch, things are going really well for you. In the classroom, however, it's a different story. You've started skipping school to play football instead, and when do you go, you just sit there staring out of the window, thinking about new tricks and waiting for the bell to ring. 'What's the point of studying,' you ask yourself, 'when I'm going to become a professional footballer?'

As your grades start to slip, your teacher warns you: 'Football is fun but it's not important, Cristiano. Education is important.'

Really? You disagree – football is important! Your parents try a different technique. 'Look son, we know how much you love playing football,' your mum tells you, 'and we don't want to stop you. But unless your grades get better, we'll have to take you off the team.'

Nooooo...

DECISION TIME

Do you:

a) Start working harder on your schoolwork as well as your skills work?

or

b) Ignore your parents – who cares about school anyway? You're going to be a football star!

For a), go to page 38
For b), go to page 40

With a bit more focus in class, your grades soon go up again. Phew! You're allowed to keep playing and your team keeps winning. You win the league title, and it feels like your football career is about to lift off.

But despite all of your man-of-the-match displays, none of the bigger clubs in Madeira ever send scouts to watch you play.

'Why not?' you ask yourself angrily. 'What's wrong with me?'

Your dad tries his best to get you another trial at Andorinha, but the team just aren't looking for any more skilful wingers.

'I'm sorry, Cristiano,' he says to you after searching everywhere. 'We'll try again next year, I promise.'

Unfortunately, the next year, the answer is the same. You're disappointed, of course, but you carry on playing for your local team, while also working hard on your studies. Although your professional football dream hasn't worked out, it's not all bad news. You realise that as much as you love playing football with your friends, there are other things you love too, like science. And now that you've turned things around at school, your grades are good enough for you to go to university to study your favourite subject – physics. The future is yours; one day, you could even become an astronaut!

THE END

Your parents warned you! When they see that your grades aren't getting any better, they take you out of the team.

'No, you can't do this!' you shout angrily at them. In that awful moment, it feels like your life is over.

'Son, it's just for a few weeks,' your mum reassures you. 'As soon as you're doing well at school again, you can go back and play.'

'That's so unfair!' In your head, you imagine your team struggling without you, losing lots of games and missing out on the league title.

But once you've calmed down a bit, you can see that you only have yourself to blame. And you know what you need to do to put things right – focus on your studies.

When you get three good grades in a row, at last your parents say that you're allowed to return to the football pitch. Hurray! But by then, your team's title dreams are already over. You carry on playing and chasing your dream, but sadly that's as good as it gets for your football career.

THE END

You're not going to let your brutal first session put you off following your big football dream. Yes, you're a bit bruised, but by the time the next session comes around, you're feeling fired up and ready to try training at Andorinha again. And that turns out to be a great decision because, on this occasion, playing against bigger, stronger kids really brings out your competitive spirit.

'Today, my team is going to win!' you tell yourself as the practice match kicks off.

Remembering the lessons from last time, you fight harder to win the ball and harder to keep hold of it too. If you find space, you show off your skills, but when you see three tall defenders towering over you, you look up and play a simple pass to a teammate instead.

'That's it – much better, Cristiano!' you hear the coach clap and cheer.

Now, he's really impressed with your ability. After a few more successful training sessions, he decides that you're ready to play in Andorinha's next match.

'Thanks, Coach!' you say as he hands you a light blue shirt of your own. You can't wait to wear it and help your team to win.

You start off as a super sub, but soon, you're the star of the Andorinha attack. Sometimes, your teammates just give you the ball and then stand back and watch in amazement. What a wing wizard you are! You're as quick with the ball at your feet as you are without it, dazzling defenders with your magical dribbling. But you've now got more to your game than just skill because you're getting better and better at shooting too.

Gooooooooooooooooooaaaaaaaaaaaaaaaalllllllllllll llllllllllllll!!!!!!!!!!!!!!!!!!

Gooooooooooooooooooaaaaaaaaaaaaaaaalllllllllllll llllllllllllll!!!!!!!!!!!!!!!!!!

'Well played, Cry Baby!' Ricardo, your teammate, shouts to you after another man-of-the-match performance.

Although you don't really like your new nickname, you understand that it's just a friendly joke. They know that you only cry sometimes because you care so much, because you're so determined to win and to become the best footballer in the world.

The first step is becoming the best player on your team, and it doesn't take you long to reach that level. When you're on fire, you can win games on your own, weaving your way through an entire team of defenders. What would they do without you?

Word soon spreads about you, Andorinha's amazing young winger. Scouts start coming to watch you play, including your godfather, Fernando, who now works for C.D. Nacional, one of the biggest clubs in Madeira. It's only when Fernando arrives at the game that he realises that it's you that everyone's talking about. He hasn't seen you in a few years and it's not just your size that has changed since then.

'Wow, when did he become so good at football?' your godfather wonders to himself as he watches you score another great goal.

After the final whistle, Fernando is desperate for you to sign for Nacional, rather than their rivals, C.S. Marítimo. But which club will you choose? Although the Marítimo Stadium is much closer to your house, in the end you decide to go where you feel most wanted.

'You're going to love it here,' your godfather tells you as he shows you around the Nacional youth academy facilities.

You nod your head eagerly as your eyes scan the perfect green pitches and the gleaming new gym equipment. Yes, you've definitely made the right decision.

But in many ways, joining Nacional is like starting all over again. You've got new teammates to compete with, new coaches to impress, and the level is a lot higher than it was at Andorinha.

'If you listen to the coaches and learn from them, this could be the start of something amazing,' your dad tells you and you agree without a doubt in your mind. Even at the age of ten, you know that you are destined for the top.

However, during your first training session, your confidence gets the better of you. When your new Nacional teammates call out for the ball, you ignore them completely and dribble towards goal on your own. You're determined to prove yourself straight away with a moment of magic. But after a few fancy

tricks and stepovers, a defender tackles you and you lose the ball.

'Why didn't you pass?' your teammates moan. And even though you're the new kid, you decide to say what you really think: 'Because I'm better than all of you!'

You're making a bad first impression and it only gets worse. Rather than learning your lesson, you try to make up for your mistake with another solo dribble. And another, and another…

By the end of the session, you're officially Nacional's least popular player. Oh dear, what are you going to do? Just as you're about to go home, the coach comes over to give you some advice. 'You have a very special talent,' he tells you kindly, 'but unless you learn to play with others, you won't succeed.'

All week, you think about your manager's words. He's right, you realise; football is a team game and you won't get very far on your own. You have to start trusting the players around you, otherwise there's no way that you'll win trophies.

At the next training session, you try to pass the

ball more often, and you see that all your teammates are really talented players too. When you work together, you score every time. You're unstoppable.

'Excellent, Cristiano,' the coach encourages you. 'Remember, that's how easy football can be!'

Now that you've found your feet at Nacional, nothing can stop you. First, you light up the local leagues with your skills and goals, and then you lead your team to victory in the regional Under-13 championships. With every game you play, there are more top football scouts watching. 'What's next for Madeira's young magician?' – suddenly that's the question that everyone around you is asking.

'Cristiano's too good to stay on this island,' Fernando declares, and your dad agrees. But where will you go instead? Well, they tell you, if you really want to follow your football dream, you may have to leave home and move to one of Portugal's biggest cities, like Lisbon or Porto. Woah, that idea seems so scary; you're still only twelve years old and you've never even left Madeira before.

'Don't worry, son,' your parents reassure you.

'Let's just see what happens.'

But when Sporting Lisbon send a scout to watch you play, suddenly things start moving really fast. 'I've never seen anyone with so many skills,' the scout reports back, before asking you to come to Lisbon for a trial.

Wow, there's a lot for you to think about because Sporting are one of Portugal's most successful teams. This would be an amazing opportunity for you.

'That's where Luís Figo started his career,' you tell yourself, 'and now look at him – he's playing for Barcelona!' Figo is one of your heroes, so it would be incredible to follow in his footsteps. But are you really ready to leave home and move to Lisbon in order to chase your football dream?

DECISION TIME

Do you say:

a) 'Yes please – Lisbon, here I come!' What if this trial is your only chance?

or

b) 'Thanks for the offer, but I want to stay in Madeira for a few more years.' You're still young and surely there will be plenty more opportunities to pursue your dream in the future.

For a), go to page 79
For b), go to page 50

Sporting Lisbon understand your decision to stay in Madeira for now. 'But if you change your mind about coming for a trial, just let me know,' the club scout says, giving his phone number to your parents.

Phew! It's a relief to know that you haven't wasted your only chance of playing for one of Portugal's biggest clubs. For now, you can go back to starring for Nacional and winning games and trophies with your friends. Then in a few years' time, maybe you can think again about making the big move to Lisbon.

On the island of Madeira, nothing stays secret for long. Soon, everyone knows about your big decision. 'Hey, look,' you see people whispering and pointing, 'that's the kid who said no to Sporting!' You try not to let it bother you, but it does. Have you made a terrible mistake? No, you remind yourself; you have to do what feels right for you.

For the next few years, Madeira will remain your home. Although Nacional aren't as famous and successful a football club as Sporting Lisbon, their senior team still plays in the *Segunda Divisão*, the second-best league in Portugal. If you keep working your way up from the academy to the first team, one day you could become the local hero who leads them all the way to the *Primeira Liga!*

'You'd be a Nacional legend forever!' Fernando, your godfather, tells you and that idea is very tempting.

There is one other option, though – moving to Madeira's biggest and best football club, Marítimo. Not only does their senior team play in Portugal's top division, but they also play in the UEFA Cup, against top teams from all over Europe. How cool would that be?! If you play well in that competition, who knows what could happen – maybe Barcelona would buy you, just like they did with your hero, Luís Figo.

You're interested, and so are Marítimo. Their scouts have been watching you for years, and now that you're 'the kid who said no to Sporting', they decide to make their move. 'If you sign for us,' they promise you, 'we'll help you become a superstar. You'll be playing in the Primeira Liga by the age of eighteen, no problem!'

Wow, isn't that what you've always dreamed of? There is one problem, though, and it's a big one –

Marítimo are Nacional's biggest rivals. Are you really ready to turn your teammates into enemies for the sake of your football career? Your godfather won't be happy either; Fernando still works for Nacional and he was the one who urged the club to sign you in the first place!

DECISION TIME

Do you:

a) Decide to stay loyal to Nacional and try to lead them up to Primeira Liga?

or

b) Accept the offer from Marítimo and then deal with the consequences later?

For a), go to page 53
For b), go to page 72

'I'm so glad that you've decided to stay,' your coach at Nacional tells you, looking both delighted and relieved at the same time. 'This is where you belong, kid – you're our future superstar!'

By the time you're fourteen, however, the club feels a little too comfortable and your football focus starts to slip. At Nacional, you know that you're one of the best players and so you take it easy in training, turning up late and putting in a lot less effort. It's not like they're going to drop you from the team, is it? They need you! But before long, the coach is fed up with you misbehaving and messing around with your mates, instead of listening to his instructions.

'Cristiano, I won't say it again – pay attention!' he calls out angrily. 'You're wasting my time and you're wasting your talent. If you don't get your act together soon, you can find another team to play for.'

Although the coach looks furious, you decide not to take his warning seriously. 'Nacional should feel lucky to have a future superstar like me!' you think to yourself arrogantly. Even when you don't work hard in training, you're still the best player on the pitch every weekend. So, what's the problem? Why can't you have fun and win football matches at the same time?

When some of your best friends decide to quit the team because they think it's boring, they urge you to forget about football and hang out with them instead.

'Cool, see you there!' you reply. Your favourite sport doesn't feel that important anymore.

But while you're skipping your practice to mess around with your mates in the park, others around you are improving. Suddenly, defenders are tackling you every time and the Nacional coach is taking you off at half-time because you're not fit enough to last the full match. What's going on? You haven't scored a goal in weeks!

Eventually, the moment arrives that you thought would never happen: your coach makes the big decision to drop you to the bench. 'Sorry Cristiano, but right now, we've got better players who deserve a chance to start.'

DECISION TIME

Do you:

a) Find your football focus again? When the Nacional coach calls on you, you're determined to make up for your bad behaviour and become your team's super sub. Your days of taking it easy are over.

or

b) Say, 'Whatever, I quit!' and storm off to hang out with your friends instead? That's way more fun, anyway.

For a), go to page 58
For b), go to page 56

Although you still like football, it's no longer your favourite thing in the world. There are so many other things in life, and you want to explore them.

At first, you really enjoy the freedom of doing what you like when you like. Sometimes, you still play a bit of football, but mostly, you sleep and hang out with your friends in the park, listening to music and messing around. That's fun for a while, but you're still the competitive kid you used to be. You still have that desire to be the best and win.

When you leave school at the age of sixteen, you get a job in a local café, where you meet João, a colleague who plays football for a small local team. He invites you to come and train with them and you think, 'Why not?' It's been a long time since you played proper football, but you haven't lost your magic touch. By the end of the first session, you're the team's new star signing!

It's nice to be playing for a club again, even if it's not Sporting Lisbon. After a strong first season, you move to another team in Madeira. They're in a higher division and they even pay you for every match that you play and every goal that you score. It's not a lot of money but still – it's always nice to have a little extra.

THE END

When your coach notices that your attitude has improved, he decides to give you another chance. He brings you off the bench with your team drawing 0–0.

As soon as the pass arrives, you burst forward down the wing, your legs a blur of fast movement and yet the ball still glued to your boot. Yes, the old Cristiano is back! After a clever turn, you look up and spot your teammate in space in the middle. Your cross is perfect!

Gooooooooooooooooooaaaaaaaaaaaaaaalllllllllllllllllllllllllll!!!!!!!!!!!!!!!!!!

Super sub to the rescue – you've won the game for Nacional with another moment of magic. 'Welcome back!' your teammates cheer and your coach gives you a pat on the back. All is forgiven and it feels good. There'll be no more distractions stopping you from achieving your dream.

Now that you've found your football focus again, you progress quickly through the Nacional youth teams until one day, the first team coach invites you to come and train with the senior squad. Wow – this is the moment that you've been waiting for, and dreaming of since you were a young boy! You're still only sixteen and it's only one training session, but still, you're determined to make the most of your opportunity. It could be all you need to succeed.

You've watched the Nacional first team train lots of times before, but now you're training *with them.* As you enter the dressing room, you feel a little bit nervous, but mostly super excited. You just hope that the players are friendly, instead of just ignoring the new kid.

'Hi, what's your name?' the Nacional captain asks, coming over to shake your hand.

'Cristiano. Cristiano Ronaldo,' you say, trying to sound as confident as you can. You don't want to seem weak in front of the team's big, strong leader.

'Nice to meet you, Cristiano. What position do you play?'

'I'm a winger,' you reply.

'Okay, so you've got lots of skills, have you?'

You nod eagerly and allow yourself a little smile. The Nacional first team players will find out soon enough. You perform well in all the training drills, but you make sure to save a little something extra for the practise match at the end. That's your time to shine.

As soon as the game kicks off, you call confidently for the ball, but the first team players don't trust you yet. Although you keep moving into space, it's like you're invisible to them. At last, one of your teammates spots you and plays a powerful pass. Your first touch is good, but as you look up, you see one of the Nacional midfielders racing towards you, wanting to welcome you to the team with a fierce tackle. You've got some quick thinking to do. You fake to pass to the right, but just as the midfielder slides in, you drag the ball across to your left foot and you're away.

'The boy's made you look like a fool there!' you hear one of the players shout.

But you don't have much time to enjoy your magic moment. Soon, there's another opponent blocking your path to goal. What next?

DECISION TIME

Do you:

a) Try another of your tricks? This is your big chance to impress, so the more skills, the better.

or

b) Play a simple pass? The coach has already seen that you're skilful, but you want him to know that you're a good team player too.

For a), go to page 62
For b), go to page 64

You find the nutmeg doesn't work and neither do the fancy flicks. Soon, your teammates are fed up with you giving the ball away all the time. Who is this cocky kid who already thinks he's a superstar?

'Pass!' they shout but you panic and make another mistake. The coach has seen enough. At the end of the training session, you're sent back to the Under-18s and that's where you stay. You've wasted your big opportunity, and as hard as you try, there's just no way back for you at Sporting.

Luckily, however, another Lisbon club give you a second chance. Although Sport União Sintrense don't play in Portugal's top divisions, at least your football career isn't over. You work hard in training and learn your Sporting lesson – keep things simple, and don't try too many tricks. At the age of eighteen, you make your first-team debut and a year later, you're the team's star attacker. You try your best to get Sintrense promoted to the Second Division, but sadly you don't quite manage it. However, there's good news for you – your skilful performances have caught the eye of Estrela da Amadora. They're in the *Segunda Liga* for now, but they're aiming for promotion – that's why they want to sign you!

In your very first season at the club, you help them achieve that target, and in the second, you help them finish mid-table in Primeira Liga. However, after that, Estrela da Amadora slip further and further down the table each year, until eventually you get relegated. Sadly, that's the end of your time in Portugal's top division, but at least you had those four, unforgettable years.

THE END

The Nacional first team coach is impressed. Not only have you got all the skills, but you also know when and where to use them. That decision-making is rare to see in such a young player.

'Well done today,' he tells you as you're about to go home. 'See you back here for tomorrow's session.' Congratulations, you've been called up to the first team! For the first few weeks, you focus on learning as much as you can from the more experienced players around you. The more you train with them, the more they trust you. They can see that you're dedicated and determined to become a star.

'You're doing all the right things,' the captain assures you when he sees you staying behind to practise your shooting. 'Now, you just have to take your opportunity when it comes.'

You try your best to stay patient, but before long, you're desperate to make your first team debut. You're ready and you're willing to play any position – even goalkeeper! But eventually, the right opportunity arrives. Ahead of their *Segunda Liga* game against Chaves, Nacional have an attacking

injury crisis. The manager finds three fit forwards who can start the game, but there'll be no back-up on the bench, unless…

Congratulations, you're named as one of the Nacional subs! For the first half and most of the second, you sit restlessly on the sidelines, waiting and hoping to come on. Then, with twenty minutes to go, your team concedes a goal. Uh oh! Although you obviously want Nacional to win, you are secretly a little pleased because now you know that your manager will have to act. Nacional need to bring on a new attacker and you're the only one on the bench!

'Ronaldo, get ready!' the assistant coach calls out to you.

In a flash, you're down on the touchline, tucking in your black–and–white striped shirt, and taking a long, deep breath. It's like your first training session all over again; you feel a little bit nervous, but mostly super excited. You've been looking forward to making your first team debut for ages and now the moment has finally arrived! But while playing football is always fun, you know that you've got a job to do. Nacional need you to create a moment of magic, otherwise the team are heading for a disappointing defeat.

So, what can you do to help? The next few minutes tick by and you still haven't touched the ball. You keep calling for it, but it never arrives. Oh well, if no-one's passing to you out on the wing, you'll have to go and get the ball yourself. You race over to steal it off the Chaves midfielder, and then with a burst of speed, you're away! You dribble forward, moving closer and closer to the penalty area until the defenders have no choice but to come out and close you down. What next? You can hear the Nacional striker to your left, calling for you to pass, but at the same time, it's very tempting to go for a wondergoal yourself…

DECISION TIME

Do you:

a) Play the pass? Your teammate is an experienced goal scorer and he's in a better position to shoot and score.

or

b) Go for goal yourself? You won the ball in the first place, so you deserve a chance to get the glory.

For a), go to page 68
For b), go to page 70

Your pass is perfect, and the Nacional striker fires the ball into the net. GOAL – 1–1! As he runs away to celebrate, he points over at you with a big smile on his face. 'Thanks, what a run!' he cheers, giving you a great big hug. Congratulations, you're on your way to becoming a Nacional hero!

The next season, you settle into the starting line-up, and lead your local team all the way to the *Primeira Liga*, just like you always said you would. What a feeling! Everyone in Funchal is so proud of you, especially your family and your godfather, Fernando. 'You did it!' they cheer happily.

You can't wait to play in Portugal's top division, against teams like Porto, Benfica, and of course, Sporting Lisbon. You start well, with a goal and two assists in your first five games, but you can't keep your good form going. You're up against better defenders now, who don't give you time on the ball to try your tricks. You finish the season with only four goals and six assists and unfortunately, Nacional are relegated. That turns out to be your team's one and only season in the top division, but it's more than enough to make you a club legend.

THE END

You trick your way past the first defender, but not the second, who tackles you before you can pass the ball. 'I was right there!' your teammate screams at you, his eyes wide with fury. 'Sorry,' is all you can say as you chase back to defend. You do your best to make up for your mistake, but sadly, the match ends in defeat. And when the manager picks his squad for the next match, you're not even named on the bench. You carry on training at the club for one more year, but it's clear that your Nacional career is over.

Eventually, you move on to sign for another football club in Madeira, U.D. Santana, down in Portugal's third division. Although you're not really looking forward to it, you find that you actually love playing at a lower level. You have more time and space to dazzle defenders with your dancing feet, before scoring and setting up goals. You enjoy being the best player on the pitch, and no-one tells you off for trying to entertain the crowd. Perfect! So even when you get offers to go and play for bigger clubs, you say no and stay at Santana.

THE END

'Welcome to our club!' the Marítimo youth coach tells you as you arrive for your first training session. 'I hope you're ready for a challenge?'

You nod eagerly – that's why you're here! You can't wait to get started and show off your silky skills. Marítimo feels like the best of both worlds – you get to stay at home in Madeira with your family, while also playing for one of Portugal's top teams. What could be better than that? Although you're still very young, your sights are set on starring in the *Primeira Liga* one day soon. You're confident that you can perform well in your country's highest league. You've got the talent *and* the self-belief. You're going to be the next Luís Figo!

When the training session begins, however, you realise that it's going to be harder than you thought to achieve your dream. Not only do Marítimo have lots of other gifted young players, but they all seem to know each other really well. They laugh and joke together as if they've been best friends forever, just like you used to with your teammates at Nacional. Oh dear, was moving to Marítimo a massive mistake?

'No,' you tell yourself, clenching your fists with determination. 'This is where I need to be.'

You do your best to show off your all-round game – your full range of flicks and tricks and also your running, passing and crossing. You're a team player who really wants to win. Surely, that's clear from all your great goals and amazing assists in the practice matches? But as the months pass by, you still feel like you're the new kid at the club. Although your teammates aren't nasty to you, they never invite you to their parties, and the Marítimo coach keeps using you as a super sub instead of putting you in the team from the start. No way, you're much better than that – you're Madeira's young magician! But how are you going to prove it when you only get to play a few minutes at the end of each match?

DECISION TIME

Do you:

a) Decide to give up on your football dream? You've tried your best, but you just can't see a way to make it at Marítimo. And you can't go back to Nacional – that would be way too embarrassing! You're only fourteen years old; there's still plenty of time to focus on your other talents.

or

b) Keep going until you break into the starting line-up, however long that takes? Remember, you're the most competitive kid in Funchal and playing professional football is your dream. Make the most of every minute on the pitch and show the Marítimo coach the amazing things that you can do with the ball at your feet.

For a), go to page 75
For b), go to page 77

It's a shame to see all your hard work go to waste, but perhaps professional football wasn't for you, after all. You go back to playing with your friends in the street, which you find much more fun anyway. Your new-found freedom makes you happier and gives you time to think about your other passions. What would you like to focus on instead of football? You decide to study hard at school so that one day you can start your own sports clothing business. That's what you're really interested in – creating cool new designs, being your own boss, and making lots of money.

You start small, selling T-shirts in the local market, but within a few years, you're successful enough to open your own sports clothing shop. Everyone really likes your designs, including the tourists who come to Madeira on holiday. Soon, you're getting online orders from all over Portugal, and all over Europe. Then comes your proudest achievement – Benfica, one of your country's biggest football clubs, asks you to create their kit for the new season!

So, although you didn't make it as a professional footballer, you still get to be involved at the top level of your favourite sport.

THE END

With your fierce determination, you finally fight your way into the starting line-up. And once you get there, nothing can stop you now. By the age of sixteen, you're one of Marítimo's most exciting young talents; by the age of eighteen, you're making your *Primeira Liga* debut, just like you'd always planned it. Congratulations, you're a professional footballer!

The first few years of your career, however, are very frustrating. While you show moments of your magic, you struggle to star consistently in the Marítimo first team. You begin to wonder whether you'll ever be more than a second-half super sub. Eventually, however, things do get better. A new manager comes in who sees your potential. He lets you start ten games in a row and that helps you to settle into life in the *Primeira Liga*. You're now a few years older and wiser, and it shows in your performances on the pitch. Thanks to your goals and assists – and, of course, skills! – you become a key part of the Marítimo team.

Although you never get your dream move to Sporting Lisbon or Barcelona, or play in Europe's biggest competitions, you enjoy a good, long career in

Portugal's top division.

THE END

As your flight takes off, you shut your eyes and try to stay calm. It's not easy, though; you're leaving Madeira for the first time in your life, on your own, to go for a trial at one of Portugal's greatest football clubs. It's the most exciting thing that's ever happened to you.

When you land in Lisbon, Sporting's chief scout, Aurélio Pereira, is there to meet you and take you to the training ground. During the drive, you sit there silently, staring out of the window at the streets you pass, crowded with cars and people. Wow, is this busy city really going to be your new home? No, you're getting ahead of yourself; first, you need to perform well at the trial. This is a massive opportunity and you have to make the most of it. That's a lot of pressure for a football-mad kid to handle, but fortunately your nerves start to fade away once you put on the Sporting kit and walk out onto the pitch. You believe in yourself; this is what you were born to do.

Soon, you're impressing everyone at Sporting with your sublime skills. Right foot, left foot – with two quick taps of the ball, you dart between two opponents and then skip past another after a deadly double stepover. Just when it looks like you're surrounded by defenders, you somehow manage to escape. You change direction with a clever drag-back turn and play a perfect pass through to your new teammate.

Gooooooooooooooooooaaaaaaaaaaaaaaaallllllllllll llllllllllllll!!!!!!!!!!!!!!!!!!!

'Wow!' you hear one player mutter. 'That's special.' With words like that, your confidence grows, and you start to feel bold and brave. So far, you've stayed calm and quiet, but why shouldn't you be yourself? Eventually, you can't hold back any longer. You release your competitive side, telling your teammates what to do and where to go, even though you're the new kid at the club. You can't help it; you want to win so much.

The Sporting youth coaches are very impressed by your talent and your attitude. After a few days of your trial, they've already made their decision. You're exactly what they're looking for – so, how soon can you sign the contract?

Wow, really?! Everything's moving so fast. Your mind is full of questions, but thankfully Aurélio explains everything to you and your parents at a meeting back in Madeira. You'll live with the other academy players at the Sporting centre, going to school during the day and then playing football every evening and all weekend. The club will even pay you a wage that will help look after your family.

'Sounds good to me!' you say with a smile as you sign your first Sporting contract. This is the chance of a lifetime.

It's hard leaving your family behind in Funchal, but you try to stay positive as you say your goodbyes at the airport.

'Good luck!' your mum says, wiping away her tears. She can't help worrying about you, her twelve-year-old son, all alone in the big capital city. However, she's happy for you and knows that Lisbon is the best place for you to be to follow your football dream. Besides, you'll be back soon to visit.

You arrive at the Sporting academy full of positivity and purpose, but those feelings don't last long. Soon, you're so lonely and homesick that you call your parents and ask to come home.

'I don't have any friends because everyone's a lot older than me,' you cry into the phone. 'And everything's just so difficult and different here!'

'Don't give up, my darling,' your mum tells you. 'Things will get better, I promise.'

She's right, of course. The Sporting youth coaches are kind and help you to settle in. Plus, you're playing so much football and performing so well, that you soon stop thinking about Madeira. Instead, you're 100 per cent focused on the career path in front of you. If you keep improving at such a rapid rate, you could be training with the first team in a few years. So, you spend every spare hour improving your game – your skills, your shooting, your fitness and your strength. No-one else works as hard as you do; that's because no-one else wants to become a Sporting superstar as much as you do.

And despite the occasional argument or selfish dribble, you're on track to reach your target in record time. By the age of sixteen, you're playing well for the Under-16s, Under-17s, Under-18s and Reserves. The only team you're not yet playing for is the first team. It's probably only a matter of time before the Sporting coach, László Bölöni, calls you up to train with his squad, but patience isn't one of your strengths. When your friend and rival, Ricardo Quaresma, joins the first team before you, it feels like you've been left behind. It doesn't matter that he's two years older than you. You don't want to wait your turn; you want to play with the big boys now.

However, when your opportunity finally arrives, you find that you're too nervous to play your best football. Training with your heroes is a lot harder than you thought it would be, especially as you're putting so much pressure on yourself to impress. You're not doing much wrong, but you're also not doing anything amazing, and that's making you more and more frustrated.

'I need to start showing Bölöni how good I can be, before it's too late!' you complain to Aurélio, who has come down to watch you practise.

Fortunately, the Sporting scout has some excellent

advice to give you: 'Where has your passion and confidence gone? You need to become fearless again.'

Yes, Aurélio's right! You've been keeping calm and quiet, rather than playing your natural game. It's time for that to change. At the next training session, you're like a totally different player. You dare to do your normal stepovers and nutmegs, even against the most experienced defenders. And when you don't have the ball, you're not afraid to fight for it, no matter who you're up against.

'Hey, who do you think you are, kid?' one of the senior players asks you angrily when you foul him by mistake.

This time, you don't stay silent, or say sorry. No, that's not your style. Instead, you tell the truth: 'I'm going to be the best player in the world.'

Wow, it's a bold move to make when you're still only sixteen, but it works! Yes, there is more for you to learn about tactics and teamwork, but you're excelling in two key areas: talent and self-belief. And that's enough to impress your manager.

'Cristiano will be better than Eusébio and Figo,'

Bölöni announces ahead of the new season.

Woah, the pressure's really on you now! But that's okay because you're confident that you can cope with the expectations. Wearing Sporting's Number 28 shirt, you make your *Primeira Liga* debut as a second-half substitute against Braga. Although the match ends in a disappointing 4–2 defeat, you show enough of your skills to earn a starting spot in the next game against Moreirense. You can't wait. You're on the right wing and your old youth team rival, Ricardo, is on the left. It's time for you to shine.

Midway through the first half, your team wins the ball near the halfway line. You race forward on the attack, calling 'Pass!' When it arrives, you're off, using your speed to burst past one player and then your skill to skip past a sliding tackle. As you approach the edge of the penalty area, you let your long legs dance. With a stepover to the left, you shift and go right instead. What a run! You're into the box now, with just the goalkeeper to beat. As he dives down in front of you, you chip the ball cheekily over him and into the empty net.

Gooooooooooooooooooaaaaaaaaaaaaaaallllllllllll lllllllllllllllll!!!!!!!!!!!!!!!!!!!

What a way to score your first league goal! You're so overwhelmed with excitement that you take off your shirt and throw it into the crowd. A Sporting superstar is born.

After that man-of-the-match performance against Moreirense, the whole football world is watching you. By the end of your first season, you've added four more goals and five assists too. Not bad for a seventeen-year-old! All of Europe's top clubs are already desperate to sign you, including Inter Milan, Real Madrid and Manchester United.

United are one of the most famous football clubs in the world. They have an incredible team – Rio Ferdinand, Paul Scholes, Ryan Giggs, Ruud van Nistelrooy – and they've just won the Premier League title for the eighth time in eleven years. However, their right winger, David Beckham, has moved to Real Madrid, and apparently, their manager, Sir Alex Ferguson, wants you to replace him. Wow! Really? 'Becks' is one of the best in the game. But it's true; United are so desperate to sign you that they've agreed to come to Lisbon to play a pre-season friendly against Sporting. Your teammate Ricardo has just been bought by Barcelona, and so your manager moves you into his starting line-up against Manchester United. You're about to face what could be your future football club, just as long as you play well…

DECISION TIME

Do you:

a) Try to show off as many skills as possible while you're on the pitch? You don't care about the result and your deal with Manchester United is almost done anyway.

or

b) Work as hard as you can to make sure that your team comes out on top? This is a great chance to impress Ferguson, your future manager, and show him that you've got a winning mentality as well as

wonderful skills.

For a), go to page 89
For b), go to page 92

You make a strong start to the game, doing lots and lots of stepovers, but after the first ten minutes, the Manchester United defenders work out how to stop you. Every time you get the ball, both John O'Shea and Rio Ferdinand rush over and block your path to goal. You could pass it to one of your teammates, but they can see that you're not in a sharing mood. Just as the defenders predicted, you keep trying to dribble your way through instead.

'Stop showing off!' João Pinto, the Sporting striker, screams as you lose possession yet again.

The more you try to make up for your mistakes, the worse things get. Your teammates stop passing to you because they know that you won't pass back. Uh oh, this has turned into a disaster! At half-time, the Sporting manager takes you off. He's had enough of your selfish skills, and so has Sir Alex Ferguson, the Manchester United manager.

'The kid's really talented, of course, but he does too many tricks,' Ferguson tells his assistant, Carlos Queiroz. 'That won't work in the Premier League. I've changed my mind – I don't think Ronaldo's what we need, after all.'

Sadly, your dream move to Manchester United is off, and Ferguson decides to sign Ronaldinho from PSG instead.

All is not lost, however. It turns out that your silky skills are much better suited to the *Primeira Liga* anyway. There's more space for you to try out all your tricks and with your old rival Ricardo gone, you become Sporting's star attacker. With your speed and skills, you lead your team to back-to-back league titles. What a hero! The fans at the José Alvalade Stadium adore you, and you see kids walking around Lisbon with your name on the back of their shirts. That's an amazing feeling, so why would you ever want to leave?

You decide to stay, even when Real Madrid and Barcelona come calling for you. This is your home; you're not going anywhere else. To say thank you for being such a loyal, one-club man, Sporting make you their new captain and you go on to break lots of club records, including most goals and most assists. Although you never get to play for one of Europe's biggest clubs, that's your decision and you have no regrets. You're a Sporting legend and you've won lots of trophies at home in Portugal, including the league's Player of the Year award. Congratulations!

THE END

The Sporting manager has picked you to play on the left wing this time, which means that you're up against Manchester United's right-back, John O'Shea. Yes, he's a decent defender, but can he deal with your speed and skill?

No, of course not! As soon as you get the ball, you dribble forward as fast as you can. Your legs are a blur of fast movements as you dance towards O'Shea, and yet the ball always stays glued to your boot. The United defender doesn't know what to do – you're unplayable! When he tries to push you out wide, you use your left foot to fly up the wing and cross it in for the strikers. And when he tries to push you inside, you weave your way straight past him and fire a right-foot rocket at goal. Although the keeper makes the save, you can see that United are scared of you.

'Rio!' you hear O'Shea shout to his fellow defender. 'I need more help here!'

Yes, you're showing off your skills, but only in order to help Sporting score and win. That's what matters most to you. Your teammates give you the ball as much as possible because they trust you to be their matchwinner. You're a superstar in the making. In the twenty-fifth minute, you slide an excellent pass through to left-back Rui Jorge, who races down the wing and curls the ball into the danger zone. It sails just past the stretching United centre-backs and through to Luís Filipe at the back post. GOAL – 1–0 to Sporting!

With your team winning, your magical masterclass continues. Everything you do is exciting and dangerous. As you flick the ball cheekily over O'Shea's head, he has no choice but to foul you.

'Come on, Sheasy!' Paul Scholes shouts. 'Get tight to him. What's going on?'

'It's not my fault,' his tired teammate replies. 'This kid's incredible!'

While you're busy destroying the Manchester United defence on the pitch, their manager Sir Alex Ferguson is busy sorting out the deal to buy you. Sadly, he misses the second half of your magic show. 'We're not leaving this country until we sign that boy,' the United boss tells his assistant, Carlos Queiroz.

At last, everything is agreed – for a fee of £12 million, you're a Manchester United player now. Wow, it's your dream come true! Sporting ask if they can keep you on loan for one more season, but Ferguson says no. Although you're still only eighteen, your new manager thinks you're ready to play in the Premier League straight away. To show his belief in your ability, he even gives you the famous Number 7 shirt, worn by club legends like George Best, Eric Cantona and David Beckham.

'I think you can deal with the pressure,' Ferguson says with a smile.

But before you can make your Manchester United debut, you've another test to get through first – training. Your new teammates take their practice sessions very seriously, especially the captain, Roy Keane. He's even more competitive than you and he's not impressed by flashy flicks and tricks. He decides to try and toughen you up before the season starts by teaching you an important lesson. So, when you attempt a sixth stepover in a row, he slides in with a crunching tackle.

'Hey!' you cry out, clutching your leg in agony on the ground.

Surely that's a foul? But no, your manager stays silent and the game goes on around you. Eventually, you pick yourself up and carry on playing. Pain isn't going to stop you from showing off your skills – that's who you are, a big part of your football identity. However, you may need to start adapting to the Manchester United style of play. A few days later, as you dribble your way down the wing again, doing trick after trick, Ruud van Nistelrooy throws his arms up in frustration.

'Just cross the ball!' the striker shouts angrily at you. 'Goals win games – not skills! How do I know when to make my run through the middle, if I don't know when, or if, the ball will ever arrive?'

Those first few weeks in England are very hard for you. You're in a new city in a new country, where you don't speak the language and it seems to rain all the time. Although you're a strong, confident character, you can't help missing your easier life in Lisbon. Your new Manchester United teammates say that they're just trying to prepare you for the Premier League, but it's not the warm welcome to English football that you were hoping for. You want to show off your skills and tricks – that's what has got you this far. But your team seems to be getting annoyed and would prefer you to be more of a team player.

DECISION TIME

Do you:

a) Ignore what your teammates are saying? You're a skilful player and that's that – you're not changing your style for anyone or any club.

or

b) Listen to your teammates and adapt your game? They're not asking you to stop doing your skills; they just want you to turn your tricks into more goals and assists to help Manchester United win.

For a), go to page 97
For b), go to page 99

You're on fire in your first few Premier League games but after that, your beginner's bounce starts to fade. Although the defenders can't cope with your skills, they can push you off the ball if you take too long trying tricks. And often when you do get past them, your end product isn't that good anyway. With every cross or shot that goes wrong, the crowd's impatience grows.

'I thought this kid was meant to be incredible?' the Manchester United fans moan. 'He's got a long way to go if he wants to become the new Becks!'

When your form doesn't improve, Ferguson moves you to the bench and uses you as a super sub instead. You're much better at attacking tired defences in the second half, and so that becomes your role. You spend three seasons at United, winning the Premier League and the FA Cup, but you never become a regular starter. Eventually, Ferguson signs a new right winger to replace you, and you return to Sporting. There, you finally become a first-choice forward, and your career flourishes. At last, you find your best form again, and at last, you lift league titles with a real sense of achievement. You've earned it; there's no way Sporting would be winning so many trophies without you! By moving back home to Portugal, you've become the player you always wanted to be. Manchester United, however, is still on your mind. Although you look back fondly on your time in England, you can't help thinking it could have been even better.

THE END

Your first season at Manchester United is a mixed one, but that's okay because you're still young and you're still adapting. Looking back, you try to focus on the positives – your free kick against Portsmouth, your super-strike against Spurs, and your header to win the FA Cup Final. Yes, there are some negatives too, but they're all part of your learning curve – losing out to Porto in the Champions League and Arsenal in the Premier League, plus a red card for getting angry against Aston Villa.

'Next season, I'm going to be much better!' you tell your teammates with confidence.

You work hard in the gym, adding more muscle in your upper body so that you can battle with defenders, and more power in your legs so that you can accelerate past them. That will definitely improve your performance, but as Rio keeps telling you, it's all about goals and assists. So, you practise your shooting for hours after training and set yourself new targets.

'Last season, I scored six, so this year, I'm aiming for fifteen,' you say to Queiroz.

However, as hard as you try, it's the same old story. Even though you're trying fewer tricks, you're still not scoring enough goals and you're not creating enough chances for Ruud and Wayne Rooney either. You show flashes of your brilliance, but is that all you've got?

'Rubbish!' the Old Trafford crowd complains as you waste yet another chance to score. Although you're still young, United can't wait forever for you to improve. Time is running out for you to reach your potential. The Manchester United supporters are starting to wonder whether it's worth trying someone else on the right wing instead.

'What about Kléberson or Darren Fletcher? At least they'd do some defending as well as attacking! And there'd be a lot less diving too…'

When you talk to Queiroz, he tells you to be patient: 'Keep working hard and everything will soon fall into place.'

United's assistant manager makes it sound so easy, but surely there's more that you can do?

DECISION TIME

Do you:

a) Work as hard as you can, all day and all night, to improve your performance? Lifting weights, practising sprints, taking shot after shot from every angle – you do it all, without any help from anyone at Manchester United. It's now or never for your football career.

or

b) Work hard but also believe in yourself more? Although it might not feel that way, you're getting better with every game. If you keep learning and listening to your coaches, your time will come eventually.

For a), go to page 102
For b), go to page 104

Without the right guidance, you're doing way too much training and putting too much strain on your body. Instead of making you faster, all that running just makes your legs feel tired and heavy. And if you're not careful, you're heading for an… INJURY! As you twist your body to turn and chase after the ball in the middle of an important match, you feel an excruciating pain in your right knee. 'Argghhhhh!' you cry out in agony.

It's bad news – you've torn your cruciate knee ligament, the worst injury a footballer can get. You're out of action for nine long months – a whole season!

And when you return, you're sadly not the same player anymore. You've still got the skills, but you've lost your burst of speed. After one more year at Manchester United, you return to Portugal to play for Sporting. You hope that you'll find your form and fitness again, but you're always aware of the niggle in your knee. So, you decide to retire early and become a football physio instead. Because of your own injury problems, you've learnt a lot about fitness, injuries and how to avoid them. Now, once you've completed your studies, you'll be able to stop other players from making the same mistake as you.

THE END

Thanks to more positive thinking, you manage to finish your second Manchester United season with nine goals. Okay, so it's not the fifteen that you were aiming for, but it's still better than six! The main thing is that you're moving in the right direction. With every game, you're becoming more like a forward and less like a winger. If you keep working hard, you're confident that you can fulfil your amazing potential.

'Next season, I'm going to be much better!' you tell your teammates again, and this time, it comes true. After another slow start, you finally find your top form after Christmas. Against Bolton, you hit the post twice, before scoring two goals. The second is an absolute beauty – a series of stepovers to fool the defender, followed by an accurate finish into the bottom corner.

'That's more like it, Ronnie!' Wayne cheers as you celebrate together. It feels like the two of you are beginning to form a brilliant partnership in attack for United.

Now that you've started scoring, you can't

seem to stop. Two against Fulham, two against Portsmouth, one against Charlton, and one against Wigan in the League Cup Final.

'Wow, you're playing like a superstar now!' Ferguson praises you as you help your team win another trophy.

Your manager's right: you've reached a new elite level. You're still dribbling at defenders like you used to, but now you're making better decisions about when to pass and when to shoot. At last, you've found your final product – goals and assists. The 2006–07 season is all set to be your best one yet, but before that, World Cup troubles await you…

In the quarter-finals of the competition, your Portugal team face England. You can't wait to take on your United teammates, Gary Neville, Rio and Wayne. For one game only, you're rivals rather than friends. You're always competitive, but this is a World Cup, and so you're more determined than ever to win. No matter what.

Midway through the second half, Wayne is battling for the ball with Ricardo Carvalho, when he seems to kick out with his foot. In the heat of the match, you forget the fact that you and Wayne are Manchester United strike partners. You race straight over to the referee, yelling, 'Come on, that's got to be a red card!'

When Wayne sees that you're trying to get him sent off, he can't believe it. 'Hey, what are you doing?!' he shouts, pushing you away. But by then, it's too late. The referee is already reaching into his back pocket… RED CARD! And after all that, you then go on to score the winning penalty in the shoot-out to knock England out of the World Cup.

Uh oh, when you return to Manchester United, you're going to be national enemy number one now. It won't be easy for you. Crowds will boo you everywhere you go, just like they did to David Beckham after his red card against Argentina in 1998. And what about your promising strike partnership with Wayne. Will he ever forgive you?

DECISION TIME

Do you:

a) Say sorry to Wayne straight after the game and quickly sort things out before they get any worse? You're teammates, and together, you're going to lead United to the Premier League title.

or

b) Ask for a transfer to another club in another country? As much as you love playing for Manchester United, you don't want to apologise. You don't think you did anything wrong. It's time for you to move on, especially as Real Madrid are interested...

For a), go to page 108
For b), go to page 113

'I'm sorry, Wazza,' you say, standing outside the England dressing room, still covered in sweat. 'I didn't want it to end like that, but I did what I had to do in order to win.'

You can see that Wayne is still furious, but he's not looking for a fight. Instead, he shrugs his shoulders. 'I understand. In the first half, I tried to get you booked for diving.'

Phew, what a relief! You're not friends again yet, but you're not enemies either. That will do for now, until you're back at Manchester United.

When the World Cup ends, you know that it'll soon be time for you to return to England. You're a bit worried about going back. Surely the England fans will hate you for your argument with Wayne. You're not sure you can face it, but then Ferguson comes to Portugal and persuades you to return.

'You have to be mentally tough to be a top player,' he tells you, 'and I know you have that toughness.'

Do you? Yes! You decide to be brave and stay at Manchester United. You've got goals you need to achieve. On your first day back, you have a good chat with Wayne, which helps to clear the air. 'Ronnie, we both want the same thing. We want to win the Premier League and if we work together, we can do it!'

Once the new season starts, you're so glad that you stayed. In the first match against Fulham, Wayne scores two and you score one in a 5–1 thrashing. This is going to be your year; you can feel it. You're now older, faster, stronger and better than ever. And with you and Wayne in attack, Manchester United will be unstoppable.

By New Year, you've already got twelve Premier League goals, with Wayne four behind on eight. But most importantly, your team is top of the table. Now, you've just got to make sure you stay there. No problem, because you're totally determined to win that trophy. You score the winner at Fulham and the winner in the Manchester Derby too. When Chelsea draw with Arsenal, at last it's over – Manchester United have won the Premier League again!

As you lift the trophy at Old Trafford on the last day of the season, it's the best day of your life so far. All your hard work and perseverance has paid off –

not only are you a Premier League Champion, but you're also the PFA Player of the Year and the Young Player of the Year too.

What a year! Are you ready to relax, sit back and enjoy your success over the summer break? No! You're already thinking ahead to next season and your next challenge: 'Now, we need to win the Champions League!'

To reach your target, you know that you'll need to raise your game to an even higher level – more goals and more assists.

'I want to become the best player in the world,' you tell United's first team coach, René Meulensteen. So together, you work hard on making you an even more effective forward. All that practice really pays off – by February, you're already on twenty-seven goals for the season. It's your best total ever and you've still got three more months to go! Most importantly, though, your team is still in the race for the Premier League title and through to the Champions League knockout rounds. Can you lead United to the Double?

Of course you can! Some people are still saying that you only perform well against weaker teams, so it's time to prove that you're a big game player. You score the winner against Lyon in the Last 16, and then a brilliant bullet header against Roma in the quarters. With a battling 1–0 win over Barcelona, you and your team make it through to the Champions League Final!

It's going to be the biggest game of your life and you're up against your Premier League rivals, Chelsea. Although you'll have Wayne and Carlos Tevez alongside you in attack, you're United's main man now. Can you handle that pressure?

DECISION TIME

Do you:

a) Get rid of any nerves by getting really fired up for the final? This is war and you're determined to be the matchwinner.

or

b) Stay calm, confident and focused on winning the final? Yes, it's the biggest game of your life, but you're not going to treat it any differently.

For a), go to page 115
For b), go to page 118

Yes, your agent tells you that after your amazing performances at the 2006 World Cup, Real Madrid are interested in buying you, and Barcelona too. That's exciting news because who played for both of those big Spanish clubs? Your hero, Luís Figo! Of the two, you prefer Real Madrid. You've always dreamed of becoming a 'Galáctico', and the timing is perfect. You need a fresh start, away from England, and there's no better place to become a superstar. So, for £20million, you become Real's latest signing.

However, when you arrive in Madrid, you find that your new club is in the middle of a major transformation. Legendary playmaker Zinedine Zidane has left, and you're one of eight new signings that summer. Eight?! The new manager, Fabio Capello, is building a brand-new team, and you're just one of his many attacking options. How are you supposed to get a regular starting spot when you're up against David Beckham, Robinho, Gonzalo Higuaín, José Antonio Reyes, Raúl and the Brazilian Ronaldo? It's impossible! That first season, your team wins the Spanish league title, but you don't get many opportunities to show off your skills. Maybe you should have stayed at Manchester United, after all. You hope that things will get better soon; however during the summer, another new manager arrives at Real Madrid and makes more new signings.

You give yourself one more season to try to force your way into the starting line-up, but when that doesn't work, you move to Italy to play for Inter Milan instead. There, you win the Italian League and Cup double, before returning home to play in Portugal for the last years of your career. Although you've had lots of success, you haven't quite become the superstar that you always wanted to become.

THE END

As soon as the Champions League Final kicks off, you're chasing around the pitch at top speed like your life depends on it. You've never been so pumped up for a football match before. When Claude Makelele tries to tackle you, you dive dramatically to the floor. You've won a free kick for your team in a good position, but instead of planning how you're going to score, you get up and push Makelele aggressively in the chest.

The referee gives you a warning and so does Wayne. 'Ronnie, calm yourself down!' he yells but you don't listen. A few minutes later, you go for a silly slide tackle on John Terry and you get a yellow card. Although you know that it was a bad foul, you still argue with the referee.

'I got the ball!' you lie.

You're so desperate to do well that you're trying too hard. Instead of helping United to win, you've gone back to your old, selfish ways. You want to be on the ball all the time, the centre of attention in the Champions League Final. But you keep trying one too many tricks and fear losing possession, instead of passing to your teammates.

'Ronnie, what are you playing at?' you hear Ferguson shout angrily on the sideline. 'Get your head in the game!'

But instead of getting better, your big game gets worse. Just before half-time, you give the ball away and Chelsea attack and score. 1–0! Instead of saying sorry for your mistake, you blame your teammates. 'Why didn't you tackle Lampard there?' you scream at Rio. Oh dear, your first Champions League Final is turning out to be a disaster. Early in the second half, you're fouled on the edge of the Chelsea penalty area. You've got a free kick in your favourite shooting position, but before you can take it, you kick out in frustration, right in front of the referee. He has no choice but to reach into his pocket and pull out a second yellow card. You're off!

'Nooooooooo!' Your big night is over, and you only have yourself to blame. Without you, Manchester United don't stand a chance of fighting back. At the final whistle, Chelsea are crowned the new European Champions and your teammates won't even speak to you. Maybe you're not the best player in the world, after all. You stay at United for another few years, but you fail to lead them to another Champions League final. That was your one chance and you blew it. With a heavy heart, you leave to join Juventus, but you never forget that awful final.

THE END

Right from the kick-off, you lead Manchester United forward on the attack. You use your skill to dribble all the way up the left wing, until Claude Makelele fouls you. Free kick! Chelsea manage to clear the ball away, but you've made a bright start to the Champions League Final.

It's a tense match, but you don't get involved in any of the angry arguments. What's the point? It won't help you and United to win. Instead, you focus on scoring. A goal in the final will show everyone that you are a big game player, and one of the best in the world. But as you chase your dream, you can't let yourself get carried away.

In the twenty-sixth minute, Scholesy and Wes Brown exchange passes on the right wing. As Wes looks up to cross the ball into the box, he sees you making your move at the back post. Heading is one of the many things that you've been working on with Meulensteen in training. It's time to put your new skill into practice. As the cross comes in, you leap high above Michael Essien to meet it with your head, using your neck muscles to get lots of power on the ball and propel it towards the bottom corner of the net.

Gooooooooooooooooooaaaaaaaaaaaaaaaalllllllllll llllllllllll!!!!!!!!!!!!!!!!!!!!

You race towards the corner flag, punching the air with passion. In United's biggest game of the season, you've scored the opening goal. Yes, you're officially a big game player now.

A few minutes later, you almost set up a second goal for Carlos, but Petr Čech makes a good save. Unlucky! Then just before half-time, Chelsea go down the other end and equalise. Noooooo! It's disappointing, of course, but you don't panic. There's still plenty of time left…

However, as hard as you try, you can't create another moment of magic. The score is still 1–1 after ninety minutes, and stays like that after the thirty minutes of extra-time too. The Champions League Final goes down to a penalty shoot-out. United are relying on you to be their hero, and you're ready for the responsibility. You take your team's third spot-kick and… it's saved!

'Nooooo!'

Your first reaction is to put your head in your hands – it's a bad miss at the worst possible moment. But you can't just stand there feeling sorry for yourself; you make your way back to the halfway line to support your teammates.

'Go on, Owen! You can do it, Nani!'

They both score for United, and luckily for you, Terry misses for Chelsea. 5–5! Now, it's down to sudden death; it's so dramatic that you can hardly bear to watch. But you do, cheering your team on. 'Come on, we're going to win this!' When Edwin van der Sar saves Nicolas Anelka's shot, it's all over – your club, Manchester United, are the new European Champions! As your teammates jump and dance in the rain, you fall down on the grass. There are so many emotions running through your body, but now it's mostly joy and relief. You lay down in the centre circle and cry. You've done it; you've achieved your dream.

'Get up, we've won!' Gary shouts to you eventually. And up you get to race over and celebrate with your teammates. Your penalty miss is already forgotten; after all, you scored the goal to take the game to penalties in the first place. You're a Manchester United hero, as well as a Champions League winner.

Right, what next? Once you've recovered from a night you'll never forget, you start thinking about the future. Is there anything left for you to achieve at Old Trafford? You've won every trophy in the English game! Is it now time to move on and test yourself elsewhere? In the newspapers, there are lots of rumours linking you with Real Madrid. You have always wanted to become a 'Galáctico' like your hero Luís Figo, so what are you waiting for?

In the end, you decide to stay at Manchester United for one more year. You win a third Premier League title and a second League Cup, but you lose in the Champions League final to Lionel Messi's Barcelona. He's your biggest rival as the best player in the world, so the defeat really hurts. Over the summer, Real Madrid try to sign you again and this time, they're not taking no for an answer and they don't mind paying lots of money for you. They're sure that you're the superstar striker they need to beat Messi's Barcelona.

DECISION TIME

Do you:

a) Say goodbye to Manchester and hello to Madrid? You'll always remember your glory days at United but it's the right time for a new challenge. You'll earn more money at Real and you'll get to go head-to-head with Messi.

or

b) Say no to Real and stay at United? Okay, so Manchester isn't as sunny as Madrid, but you're settled there, starring alongside Wayne in attack. It's the perfect place for you to become the best player in the world, even better than Messi.

For a), go to page 125
For b), go to page 123

Ferguson is delighted to hear that you're staying at Manchester United and so are the fans and players. How would they win so many trophies without you?

'Right, let's go and win the Champions League again, Ronnie!' Wayne tells you with a big smile on his face.

That's exactly what you were thinking too! You score the winner to beat Bayern Munich in the quarter-finals and then you and Wayne score two goals each as you thrash Lyon 4–0 in the semis. What a deadly duo! United are through to the final again, but this time, you won't be taking on Messi's Barcelona. Surprisingly, they've lost to José Mourinho's Inter Milan.

Inter are a very well-organised and difficult team to beat. That's why Manchester United are relying on you to create a moment of magic…

Midway through the first half, you burst forward with the ball, tricking your way past Maicon with a sublime bit of skill. As you approach the Inter penalty area, you fake to pass it through to Wayne, but instead you go for goal yourself. You hit it perfectly and the ball dips and swerves past Júlio César and into the top corner

Gooooooooooooooooooaaaaaaaaaaaaaaaallllllllllll llllllllllllllll!!!!!!!!!!!!!!!!!!!!

What a wonderstrike! You really are the best player in the world and now everyone knows it. You stand there in front of the celebrating United fans, looking like the superhero you are.

Your goal is enough to win the Champions League Final. Congratulations, you're a two-time European Champion! You also win a second Ballon d'Or award, but that's as good as it gets for you. After the final, Ferguson decides to retire as Manchester United manager and things soon start to fall apart. It's not the same without him and the team slips down the Premier League table, below Chelsea and your local rivals, Manchester City. You try your best to rebuild and return to the top, but it's no use. Eventually, you wave goodbye to United and go back to play in Portugal, where your brilliant career began.

THE END

You'll miss Manchester United, but it's time for you to begin your big new adventure in Spain. Real Madrid have been trying to sign you for years, and now they've paid big money for you. In fact, the £80 million transfer fee makes you the most expensive footballer in the world. You're a Galáctico now, a Real superstar, just like you always wanted.

Wow, what a welcome! The Bernabéu Stadium is packed with nearly 90,000 passionate supporters. They're all here to see you and you're not even playing a game. As you walk out on to the pitch, wearing the club's famous white kit for the first time, the fans chant your name:

RONALDO! RONALDO! RONALDO!

You turn and wave and give two thumbs-up. You really feel like a famous superstar now. Captain Raúl already has your favourite Number 7, so instead you're wearing Number 9, the shirt worn by another club legend, Alfredo Di Stéfano. The Argentinian is Real's record scorer with 308 goals but you're ready to beat that. Once you reach the stage in the middle, you give a short speech: 'Wow, thank you, I'm so happy to be here! I always dreamed of playing for this club and now it's a reality – I'm a Real Madrid player. *Hala Madrid!*'

What a reaction! The fans clap and roar like you're a pop star who's just performed their biggest hit song. The atmosphere at Old Trafford was always amazing, but you can tell that the Bernabéu will be even better on matchday. You're going to enjoy playing for this football club; you can feel it already. After entertaining the crowd with a few keepy-uppies, you kiss the badge on your shirt. You can't wait to start starring for Real Madrid on the pitch. You're hungry for more: more goals, more assists, more glory, and more trophies.

The Real Madrid president, Florentino Pérez, is building a brilliant team to take on Messi's Barcelona. You're one of four new signings, along with midfielder Xabi Alonso, playmaker Kaká and striker Karim Benzema. Not bad! And that's just the new faces; Real already have Iker Casillas in goal, plus Sergio Ramos, Pepe and Marcelo in defence, and Gonzalo Higuaín and Raúl in attack. With such a talented team, why can't you win the Spanish League title and the Champions League?

Although the pressure is on, you don't let it bother you. What's there to feel nervous about? You're twenty-four years old now, and you've already won three Premier League trophies, plus the Champions League and the Ballon d'Or. So, as you walk out at the Bernabéu for your first La Liga match, you're full of self-belief and determined to mark your debut with a goal.

As half-time approaches, your team is drawing 1–1 with Deportivo de La Coruña. That's not good enough; only a win will do. Lassana Diarra plays a pass through to Raúl, who is fouled by the keeper. Penalty! Even though he's the captain and he earned the spot-kick himself, Raúl lets you take it. After a stuttering run-up, you… blast the ball into the bottom corner.

Gooooooooooooooooooaaaaaaaaaaaaaaallllllllllll lllllllllllllll!!!!!!!!!!!!!!!!!!

New team, same superstar – you're off the mark immediately! You punch the air with passion as your teammates rush over to congratulate you. However, you can hardly hear what they're saying because the Bernabéu crowd is making so much noise, cheering for their club's exciting new hero. That scoring feeling is even better than you'd imagined.

In your first five games, you score five goals, and Real record five wins. It's a very strong start, but your team is still tied with Barcelona at the top of the table, and unfortunately, you've picked up an ankle injury. Noooo! The timing is terrible, just as you're finding your top form in Madrid. You find it so frustrating to sit and watch your new team struggle without you, especially when they lose 2–1 to Sevilla. If only you had been out there on the pitch; you would have helped them win for sure! You try not to think about it too much. Instead, you work really hard on your recovery and count down the days until you can play again. It's good to have a target to aim for: 29 November, Barcelona vs Real Madrid. You've got to be fit in time for your first ever *El Clásico*!

When matchday arrives, it's good news; you've

made the starting line-up. Hurray! It feels so good to be back in action and you've been looking forward to your best-in-the-world battle with Messi for a long time. So, can you create a moment of magic to win the game for Real Madrid? In the first half, Kaká sets you up with a glorious chance to score, but somehow Vîctor Valdés makes the save. As the ball flies over the crossbar, you hold your hands to your head. So close! It's a big opportunity missed, and you know it. That turns out to be the best one you get because in the sixty-fifth minute, your manager decides to take you off. After your injury, you're not ready to play the full ninety minutes yet.

By then, Barcelona are winning, thanks to a brilliant volley by Zlatan Ibrahimovi⊠. 'At least it wasn't Messi!' you think to yourself as you sit moodily on the bench. But still, when your first *El Clásico* ends in defeat, you're extremely disappointed. Although Barcelona are only two points ahead, it feels like your team has lost a major battle. And as Real's superstar record signing, you feel like you've failed.

'I need to make it up to the team,' you tell yourself. Most of the time, your determination gets you goals, but sometimes, it also gets you into trouble. After scoring against Almería, you take off your shirt in celebration. That gets you a first yellow card and three minutes later, you get a second for kicking out at a defender. You're off!

It's such a silly mistake, especially as it means you have to miss the next match, an important away trip to Valencia. You apologise to your teammates and say it won't happen again, but it does, less than two months later. Your team is cruising to a comfortable victory thanks to your two goals, when suddenly you lose your temper again. This time, you get a straight red card and a two-match suspension.

'You've got to calm down,' Pellegrini, your manager, tells you. 'Defenders are trying to make you angry and you're falling for it every time!'

DECISION TIME

Do you:

a) Ignore your manager's warning and keep playing exactly the same way? You're playing well, and your competitive spirit is what makes you such a winner.

or

b) Listen to your manager and try to stay a bit calmer? Maybe you can find a way to keep your incredible will to win without getting yourself into trouble on the pitch.

For a), go to page 132
For b), go to page 134

As soon as your suspension is over, you're back with a bang. You're determined to make up for your mistake and so you score four goals in the next four games to keep Real only two points behind Barcelona.

'Come on, we can still win the title!' you tell your teammates confidently. However, before long, your temper gets the better of you once again, and this time, the consequences are much greater. Real are losing 1–0 at home against Sevilla when you're shown a second yellow card for arguing with the referee. Your team has to play with ten men for most of the second half and falls to an embarrassing 3–0 defeat. In the next game, while you're serving your suspension, they can only draw 1–1 away at Real Valladolid. Barcelona, meanwhile, are beating Valencia 3–0 thanks to another Messi hat-trick.

The league title is slowly slipping away, and the Real fans are furious. They blame you – yes, you're scoring lots of goals, but your lack of discipline is costing the team dearly. Your manager, Pellegrini, is fed up with your bad behaviour too. He decides to start Karim and Gonzalo in attack instead; at least they can be trusted to keep calm on the pitch. For the rest of the season, you watch from the bench as they form a star strike partnership, shooting Real past Messi's Barcelona to win the Spanish league title. Although you join in the celebrations, you don't feel like you really deserve your winner's medal.

During the summer, Real Madrid make more new signings. Your club buys two new attacking midfielders, Mesut Özil and Ángel Di María, plus two new forwards, Emmanuel Adebayor and a highly rated young Brazilian called Neymar Jr. What about you? Will you get any game-time? The answer is no. When AC Milan make an offer of £50 million, Real Madrid decide to accept it. You win lots of trophies in Italy, but it's not the same as being a Real superstar. That dream of yours didn't quite come true.

THE END

Once your two-game ban is over, you keep calm and get back to doing what you do best – scoring goals. When your team go 2–0 down against Sevilla, you don't react angrily and get yourself sent off again. Instead, you score a great goal and inspire Real Madrid to a remarkable 3–2 victory. That result takes you level with Barcelona at the top of the table again.

'Come on, we can win the title!' you tell your teammates confidently. All is forgiven; they can see that you've learnt your lesson and now they trust you to lead them to glory. Every game you play, you get a goal or an assist, or often both. You're on fire, but unfortunately for you, so is Messi. Real Madrid and Barcelona are still tied on seventy-seven points each, ahead of the second *El Clásico* of the season. And this time, you're playing at home at the Bernabéu. Real are relying on you to be their big game player, so can you step up and prove that you're the best in the world?

In the first half, you struggle to get into the game. Barcelona's centre back Carles Puyol is marking you closely and although you keep calling for the ball, it rarely arrives. That's mainly because Messi is running the show. In the thirty-second minute, you watch helplessly from the halfway line as he plays an amazing one-two with Xavi and then scores past Casillas. 1–0 to Barcelona, 1–0 to Messi! Uh oh, what are you going to do now? Real need you to react.

Early in the second half, at last you get the chance to shoot. Although you're on your left foot, it's almost as lethal as your right. *BANG!* It's a powerful strike, but it's straight at the keeper, who makes a comfortable save. Noooo! A few minutes later, Barcelona go up the other end and score a second goal. 2–0 – game over, title race over. You're devastated; you and your teammates have worked so hard all season, but in the most important match, you've been beaten.

You finish your first year at Real Madrid with twenty-six league goals. That's a very good total, but it leaves you eight behind Messi, who also has the La Liga title and the 2010 Ballon d'Or. He's definitely the winner… this time. As soon as one season ends, you start thinking about the next. You're determined to defeat Messi and Barcelona and so is your new Real Madrid manager, José Mourinho. He buys your Portugal international teammate, Ricardo Carvalho, to improve the defence, and then Ángel Di María and Mesut Özil to add more creativity to the attack.

You're still Real Madrid's main man, though, and your numbers are getting better and better. After nine games of the new season, you've already got eleven goals, plus six assists, which is way more than Messi. And most importantly, Real are one point ahead at the top of the table going into the biggest game of all – *El Clásico.* So far, it's two defeats out of two for you against Barcelona, and you're desperate to prevent a horrible hat-trick. Unfortunately, in a tense and angry game, there's nothing you can do to save your team from a devastating defeat…

Xavi lifts it over Casillas. *1–0!*

Pedro taps in at the back post. *2–0!*

Messi sets David Villa up twice. *3–0, 4–0!*

Jeffrén chips another shot past Casillas. *5–0!*

You can't believe what you're seeing. Yes,

Barcelona are very good, but you and the other Real Madrid players are making it far too easy for them! As each goal goes in, your frustration grows. Why does your team keep falling apart in the big games against Barcelona? Will you always be second best behind your greatest rivals?

DECISION TIME

Do you:

a) Use your rivalry with Messi and Barcelona to push yourself and your team to improve? Yes, you want to beat them, but you need to make sure you learn from your mistakes or focus on being a better player first.

or

b) Channel everything you've got into beating Messi and Barcelona. You become obsessed with winning the next *El Clásico* and finishing the season as La Liga's top scorer. Nothing else matters, other than beating your biggest rivals and

being the best striker.

For a), go to page 141
For b), go to page 139

You count down the days and months until your rematch with Barcelona. It's always at the front of your mind, even when you're playing against other teams. You're still scoring lots of goals, but that's mainly because you have to if you want to beat Messi to the top goalscorer award. Every chance you get to shoot, you take it, even if a teammate is in a better position to score. You're no longer interested in passing or defending.

With back-to-back hat-tricks against Getafe and Villarreal, you move on to twenty-two goals, still four ahead of your rival. However, your team only manages to draw both matches and so Real are now six points behind your biggest rivals. The slip-ups continue. Still, if you can beat Barcelona at the Bernabéu, you'll be happy… In the second *El Clásico* of the season, Real win 1–0 and you score the goal from the penalty spot. Hurray, at last you've beaten them! You celebrate like you've just won the league, but by then, the trophy already belongs to Barcelona. You finish the season as the league's top scorer with forty-five goals, but your team finishes fourth behind Valencia and Villarreal.

During the summer, Mourinho is sacked, and the new man in charge, Jürgen Klopp, isn't looking for a selfish striker who only cares about goals. He wants someone who's going to work hard for the team, whether you're playing against Barcelona or the club at the bottom of the league. After a bad season on the Real Madrid bench, you leave Spain and return to England to join Chelsea. However, your mind is still fixed on Messi and Barcelona, and so you're delighted when you're drawn against them in the Champions League. You're not the same player you once were, though, and your team loses 3–0, with Messi scoring two. Sadly, your best-in-the-world battle hasn't spurred you on to reach new heights; instead, you've lost your focus and your position at the top level.

THE END

Although it's hard not to think about that 5–0 thrashing by Barcelona, you and your team need to move on. The most important thing is to learn your lessons and improve. As a team, you know that you have to defend better and keep calmer in the big games. When you're all fired up, it's too easy to lose your focus. And as an individual, you need to be a bit more like Messi. When his team needs him most, he creates magic out of nothing. With your talent, it's time for you to do the same for Real Madrid.

In the very next game, you score both goals to beat Valencia – one with your left foot and one with your right.

'That's more like it!' you scream, letting out all your frustration. For the rest of the season, you work hard to help Real Madrid win as many matches as possible, whether that means scoring a hat-trick against Villarreal or setting up Marcelo away at Espanyol. It's one big team effort, and although you can't catch Barcelona in the title race this time, you can tell that Real are getting better and better. As you end the season with two goals and four assists in an 8–1 win against Almería, you feel excited about the future.

'Next year,' you tell your teammates, 'that Spanish league title will be ours!'

You won't stop until you achieve that goal. On the opening day of the 2011–12 season, you score a hat-trick in a 6–0 win at Real Zaragoza, while Messi gets two goals and an assist as Barcelona beat Villarreal 5–0. The best-in-the-world battle is on! But the most important thing for you is team trophies, not Ballon d'Ors. You use your rivalry with Messi to spur you on to become a better player. In the big games, you make the difference for Real Madrid, like when you win the derby against Atlético with two goals and an assist for Ángel. Okay, so your team loses to Barcelona at home at the Bernabéu, but this time, you and your teammates stay focused on the bigger picture. You bounce straight back to win your next eleven league games in a row. That takes Real to ten points clear at the top of the table.

Surely, the title race is over, and this is going to be your year? But you keep winning and working hard, just to make sure – 4–1 away at Atlético Madrid, 3–1 at home to Sporting Gijón… and 2–1 away at Barcelona! Revenge tastes so sweet, especially as it's you who scores the winner with a fantastic finish past Valdés.

Gooooooooooooooooooaaaaaaaaaaaaaaaallllllllllll llllllllllllll!!!!!!!!!!!!!!!!!!

After two more victories, it's official – Real are the new Spanish Champions! What a superb season it has been and what a brilliant team effort. You celebrate with a big party at the Bernabéu, followed by an open-top bus ride through the streets of Madrid. Congratulations! Messi might have beaten you to the top goalscorer and Ballon d'Or awards, but you've got the trophy you really want – the La Liga title.

Right, what next? That's what you ask yourself once the buzz of being a Spanish league-winner starts to wear off. You set your sights on winning a second Champions League trophy, to go with the one you won at Manchester United. It's a big deal, both for you and for Real Madrid because the club has been waiting ten long years to win the competition for a tenth time. For the last two seasons, you've come so close, before being knocked out at the semi-final stage, first by your rivals, Barcelona, and then by Bayern Munich.

'We can't let that happen again,' you announce ahead of the 2012–13 season. 'We're going all the way this year!'

You help your team get through the 'Group of Death' with Borussia Dortmund, Ajax and Manchester City, and then really come alive in the knockout rounds. You score two goals to beat your old club, Manchester United, in the Last 16, and then three against Galatasaray in the quarters. You're through to the Champions League semi-finals again, and again, your team slips up at the crucial moment. Away in Germany, Dortmund destroy you 4–1 and you can only win 2–0 back at the Bernabéu. Noooo! Despite your best efforts, it's the same old story for Real Madrid.

During the summer, Mourinho leaves the club and returns to Chelsea for a second spell as their manager. One night, he calls you up and asks you to join him in London. 'Together, we can win the Champions League here!' he declares confidently.

DECISION TIME

Do you:

a) Say yes and sign for Chelsea? You and your Real Madrid teammates have tried and failed to win the Champions League three times now. It's just not working, so you need to go somewhere new.

or

b) Say no and stay at Real Madrid? You don't like giving up on something; that's not your style. You told your teammates that you'd win the Champions League together and so that's what you're going to do.

For a), go to page 146
For b), go to page 148

It feels good to be back in England, even if you are wearing blue these days, rather than red. With you in attack, alongside Eden Hazard and Oscar, Chelsea storm past Manchester City and Liverpool to lift the Premier League trophy. Although it's great to win your fourth title, that's not your number one aim. Can you win the Champions League too?

The signs look good as you top your group and then storm past Galatasaray and PSG. You're through to yet another semi-final, and this time, you're up against your old Madrid rivals, Atlético. You've got a great goalscoring record against them, but Mourinho decides to play it safe and defensive away in Spain. The first leg finishes 0–0, so now you just have to win the second leg at Stamford Bridge. When you give Chelsea an early lead, you feel like you're almost through to the final. But just before half-time, Atlético start their fightback. Adrián scores the first, then Diego Costa, then Arda Turan.

Uh oh – with twenty minutes to go, your team is heading out of the tournament. You manage to score one more to make it 3–2, but after that, the Atlético defence stays strong. For the fourth year in a row, you've lost in the Champions League semi-finals.

You try again the next year, but this time, you're beaten by PSG in the Last 16. And after that, things start to go wrong for you at Chelsea. First, you fall out with Mourinho and then, when he gets sacked, the new manager, Pep Guardiola, wants to build an exciting young team that doesn't include you. After one more season at Stamford Bridge, you say goodbye to England and head to Italian giants, Napoli, for the last few years of your incredible football career. Although you lead your new club to their first Serie A title since the days of Diego Maradona, you can't add to your one Champions League triumph with Manchester United.

THE END

You're not going anywhere yet – your family is settled in Madrid and you love your football club. Plus, Real's new manager, Carlo Ancelotti, shares your Champions League ambition. He's already won the competition twice before with AC Milan, but he wants his hat-trick. And to do that, he's going to need your help. Even though Real have just signed Gareth Bale from Tottenham for £85 million, you're still their main man.

You show it by scoring nine goals in the group stage, plus four more in the Last 16 against Schalke. You're on fire! In the quarterfinals, you face Borussia Dortmund, the team that knocked you out the previous year. Not this time, though – you beat them 3–2 to set up a semi-final against Bayern Munich. Karim scores the only goal as you win the first leg 1–0 at the Bernabéu, but that still leaves you with a tricky trip to Germany. Can you hold on to your lead and make it through to the Champions League Final at last?

Yes! Real Madrid have learnt their lessons after losing so many semi-finals. Away in Munich, your team puts on a perfect performance. You're 3–0 up by half-time, thanks to two goals from Sergio and one from you. Then to complete the victory, you score a fantastic free kick in the very last minute of the match.

'Champions League Final, here we come!' you cheer.

Now, you have to go all the way and win the competition. Your opponents in the final are your local rivals, Atlético Madrid. They've just won the Spanish League title, and now they're attempting to do The Double. You can't let that happen. No way!

But with seconds to go, Atlético are leading 1–0. Just when it looks like your Champions League dream might be over, Sergio scores a header to take the game to extra-time. Phew! After that, it's all Real Madrid. First, Gareth makes it 2–1 with a header, then you set up Marcelo to score, and finally, you score yourself from the penalty spot.

Goooooooooooooooooaaaaaaaaaaaaaaalllllllllll llllllllllllll!!!!!!!!!!!!!!!!!!!

Yes, yes, yes, your dream is complete – you're a Champions League winner again! You celebrate by taking off your shirt and standing there by the corner flag, looking like The Incredible Hulk, as you roar at the sky.

You return home to Madrid as a hero. Is there anything left for you to achieve? Yes! Although you've already won two Ballon d'Ors, you want more. And although you've already won two Champions League trophies, you want more. That's just the kind of competitive character you are.

The next year, your team loses to Juventus in the semi-finals, but in 2016, you make it back to the Champions League Final. Amazingly, your opponents are the same as last time – your local rivals, Atlético Madrid. On this occasion, things are the other way around – Real score first and Atlético get a late equaliser. But neither team can score an extra-time winner this time, and so the game goes to penalties. After six spot-kicks, it's 3–3, but then Sergio scores for Real and Juanfran misses for Atlético. Now, it's your turn and if you score, your team will win the Champions League trophy. With the pressure on, you step up and… send the keeper the wrong way.

Gooooooooooooooooooaaaaaaaaaaaaaaaallllllllllllllllllllllllll!!!!!!!!!!!!!!!!!!!

You've done it again and that's your Champions League hat-trick. You take off your shirt and throw it high into the air. What a superstar you are. You've achieved so much, and you're still only thirty-one years old. What's next on your wishlist?

'Relax for a minute,' your friends and family try to tell you. 'Enjoy all your success.' Playing at the top level is really tiring, so maybe it's time for you to set out on a new adventure somewhere else. There are plenty of clubs in China or the USA who will pay you lots of money to star in their less competitive leagues.

DECISION TIME

Do you:

a) Leave Real Madrid to play at an easier level? There's nothing more for you to achieve in Europe, so why not go and help grow the game in China? It'll also give you more time to work on your other interests, like your 'CR7' fashion brand.

or

b) Stay at Real Madrid to chase more success? It's not in your nature to take it easy; you need to be challenged. Yes, you've already achieved a lot in the game, but you've still got new goals to reach, starting with leading Portugal to glory at Euro 2016.

For a), go to page 153
For b), go to page 156

You sign for Shanghai SIPG, who just finished second in the last Chinese Super League season. It's the biggest transfer in the country's history and everyone is really excited. As you arrive at the airport, you're greeted by thousands of fans, all wearing the red club colours and wanting photos with you. Wow, you feel like even more of a famous superstar here!

Although moving to China is a brave new adventure for you, at least there will be people around you who speak the same language. Shanghai SIPG's manager, André Villas-Boas, is Portuguese like you, and the club also has two players from Brazil: Elkeson and Hulk. They give you a warm welcome and make you feel at home. You're looking forward to starting your career in China, but first, you're off to France to captain your country at Euro 2016.

This could be your last chance to win an international competition with Portugal. You lost in the final at Euro 2004 and then reached the semi-finals at the 2006 World Cup, but since then, you've failed at every tournament. Can you finally give your country something to cheer about? Your team gets off to a shaky start, with two disappointing draws against Iceland and Austria. What's going wrong? You're supposed to be Portugal's star player, but you haven't scored in either game. Now that you know you're off to China, you've lost some of your sharp football focus. Still, if you can just beat Hungary, your team will make it through to the Round of 16. Early in the second half, however, Portugal are 2–1 down. You manage to equalise, but then Hungary score again straight away. 3–2! As hard as you try, you can't score again. It's another embarrassing early exit for Portugal.

Oh well, you switch your focus back to succeeding at Shanghai SIPG. As the Chinese Super League season starts, you're joined by former Real Madrid and Portugal teammate, Ricardo Carvalho. With him in defence and you and Hulk in attack, your team can't lose! In fact, you don't lose a single game all year. Shanghai SIPG set lots of new league records, including highest-ever points total (eighty) and most goals scored (102). You've got sixty-two of them, winning you the Golden Boot and the Player of the

Year award, to go with the Chinese Super League trophy.

After lifting four league titles in a row and scoring 232 goals, you wave goodbye to China and goodbye to football too. You've had an incredible career, but now it's time to focus on your 'CR7' fashion brand, which has become a big hit in China.

THE END

You've won so many trophies during your amazing career – one Spanish league title, two Spanish cups, three Premier League titles, three English cups, three Champions League trophies and three Ballon d'Ors. But it still feels like something is missing. That something is an international trophy with Portugal.

You lost in the final at Euro 2004 and then reached the semi-finals at the 2006 World Cup, but since then, you've failed at every tournament. Can you finally give your country something to cheer about? As captain, it's your job to lead the national team to glory. After two disappointing draws against Iceland and Austria, things aren't looking good. You're supposed to be Portugal's star player, but you haven't scored in either game. Still, as long as you don't lose to Hungary, you'll make it through to the Last 16.

As you've done so many times during your career, you shine when your team needs you most. The match turns out to be a crazy, six-goal thriller, and each time Hungary score, you help Portugal to fight back. First, you set up Nani with a perfect pass. *1–1!*

Then in the second half, you score two great goals of your own. The first is a fancy flick and the second is a brilliant header. *3–3!* Somehow, you've saved your team and taken them through to the next round. What would Portugal do without you?

Although your team is still not at its best, you manage to beat Croatia in the Last 16. It's your old Sporting teammate, Ricardo Quaresma, who scores the winner this time. In the quarter-finals, you defeat Poland on penalties, and suddenly, Portugal are into the semi-finals! When it comes to winning the biggest games, you're one of the best in the world. You leap high to head home the opening goal against Wales and then set up Nani to score the second. 2–0 – your team is through to the Euro 2016 final!

It won't be easy, though. In the final, you're facing the tournament hosts, France. Not only do they have the home crowd behind them, but they also have a team full of superstars like Antoine Griezmann and Paul Pogba. Portugal, however, have the best player in Europe – you! If you can just create one moment of magic, maybe you can…

But after twenty-five minutes, your game is already over. A tackle from Dimitri Payet has left you limping and despite your best efforts, you can't carry on. What a disaster for you and for Portugal! With tears in your eyes, you pass the captain's armband to Nani and then hobble off the pitch. For the rest of the final, you support your team from the sidelines. They defend well without you and after ninety minutes, it's still 0–0. Then, midway through extra-time, your super sub Éder fires in the winning goal. 1–0 to Portugal! Despite your injury, you jump up and down on the touchline. You've done it, your team are the Euro 2016 Champions! As you lift the trophy high above your head, it's yet another amazing football moment that you'll never forget.

And there are lots more to come. You win two more Ballon d'Ors to take your total to five, which leaves you tied at the top with Messi. You also win two more Champions League trophies to take that total to five too. With you leading the attack, your Real Madrid team is simply unstoppable. You win three European finals in a row!

After the last one against Liverpool, however, you think again about your future. This time, you do decide to leave Real Madrid after nine unbelievable years and 450 goals. You're thirty-three years old now, which means you've got time for one final football challenge, but where will you go?

DECISION TIME

Do you:

a) Move to Italy and chase one last Champions League trophy? You're still good enough to star in Europe's top competition and you've still got the hunger too. Juventus are a big club and they're desperate for you to help them win the Champions League.

or

b) Move to America for a different football adventure? David Beckham's new Inter Miami team have just joined the MLS and he wants you to be their big superstar signing.

For a), go to page 161
For b), go to page 164

Certainly, £100 million is a lot of money to pay, especially for a thirty-three-year-old, but Juventus know that you're worth it. The Italian giants already have an amazing defence and now with you in attack, they've got everything they need to become the best team in Europe.

You settle in straight away, wearing your favourite Number 7 shirt. You score goal after goal in Serie A to lead Juventus to their eighth league title in a row. Congratulations on yet another top trophy! That's not really why the club have signed you, though. They want to win the Champions League for the first time since 1996.

Getting through the group stage is pretty straightforward, but then you face your old rivals, Atlético Madrid, in the Last 16. They win the first leg 2–0, leaving you with lots of work to do to save the day for Juventus. But you don't panic; instead, you produce one of your finest Champions League performances.

A header in the first half. *1–0!*

Then another early in the second. *2–0!*

And finally, a cool finish from the penalty spot. *3–0!*

Congratulations, that's your hat-trick and that's your team through to the quarter-finals! It's exactly why Juventus paid so much money to sign you. When it comes to big moments in big games, there's no-one better than you.

Sadly, however, you can't do it all over again in the next round against Ajax. Juventus draw the first leg 1–1, thanks to another header from you. You then score again in the second leg, but you can't do it all on your own. For once, your strong defence is struggling, and your young Dutch opponents fight back to win 3–2. At the final whistle, you walk straight down the tunnel, feeling too frustrated for words.

Winning your sixth Champions League trophy will just have to wait. You've signed a four-year contract with Juventus, so there's plenty of time left. There's no doubt in your mind that you'll succeed eventually – you're Cristiano Ronaldo, after all, five-time winner of the Ballon d'Or and one of the best footballers ever! Until you achieve your ultimate aim, you'll keep doing what you always do: scoring goals and saving the day for your team when they need you the most.

THE END

Beckham is delighted when you agree to join his team. 'You're going to be the greatest goalscorer the USA has ever seen!' he declares.

There's just one problem; Inter Miami can't join the MLS until January 2020. That means there's a whole eighteen months for you to wait! So, until then, you sign for PSG on loan. You, Kylian Mbappé and Neymar Jr, all in the same attack – it's the most exciting strikeforce ever! You win your Champions League group with ease and then thrash your old club, Manchester United, in the Last 16. Next up: your old rivals, Messi and Barcelona.

You're not the only one feeling fired up. The other PSG players are desperate for revenge after collapsing to a 6–1 defeat at Barcelona back in 2017. Thanks to a great team performance, you win the first leg 2–0 in Paris. Kylian and Neymar Jr get the goals, and you get both assists. In the second leg in Spain, Messi scores an early goal for Barcelona, but up you jump at the back post to give PSG a crucial away goal. 'Come on!' you cheer. Even at the age of thirty-four, you've still got it. Sadly, your last Champions League adventure comes to an end in the semi-finals against Liverpool. Jürgen Klopp's side are just too strong, quick and organised for your team of superstars.

Never mind, you move on to your next challenge – conquering the MLS. You can't wait to make it big in America, just like you have in every other country you've been to. Your first match for Inter Miami is away at Los Angeles FC, one of the best teams in the league. Their star player, Mexican striker Carlos Vela, scores the opening goal, but you soon fight back. This is your debut – your big game. You equalise with a powerful header before half-time and then add two second-half strikes to win the match for Inter Miami. What a start! It's day one, and the MLS already has a new hat-trick hero.

THE END

Manchester United

- Premier League: 2006–07, 2007–08, 2008–09
- FA Cup: 2003–04
- Football League Cup: 2005–06, 2008–09
- Champions League: 2008–09

Real Madrid

- La Liga: 2011–12
- Copa del Rey: 2010–11, 2013–14
- UEFA Champions League: 2013–14, 2015–16

Portugal

- FIFA Under-20 World Cup Golden Ball: 2005

Individual

- UEFA Team of the Year: 2004, 2007, 2008, 2009, 2010, 2011, 2012, 2013, 2014, 2015
- PFA Premier League Team of the Year: 2005–06, 2006–07, 2007–08, 2008–09
- PFA Young Player of the Year: 2006–07
- PFA Players' Player of the Year: 2006–07, 2007–08
- FWA Footballer of the Year: 2006–07, 2007–08
- FIFA FIFPro World XI: 2007, 2008, 2009, 2010, 2011, 2012, 2013, 2014, 2015
- Premier League Golden Boot: 2007–08
- European Golden Shoe: 2007–08, 2010–11, 2013–14, 2014–15
- UEFA Champions League top scorer: 2007–08, 2012–13, 2013–14, 2014–15, 2015–16
- Ballon d'Or: 2008, 2013, 2014, 2016
- FIFA World Player of the Year: 2008
- La Liga top scorer: 2010–11, 2013–14, 2014–15
- La Liga Team of the Season: 2013–14, 2014–15, 2015–16
- La Liga Best Player: 2013–14
- UEFA Best Player in Europe Award: 2014, 2016

RONALDO

7

THE FACTS

NAME:
Cristiano Ronaldo

DATE OF BIRTH:
5 February 1985

AGE: 35

PLACE OF BIRTH:
Funchal, Madeira

NATIONALITY: Portugal

BEST FRIEND: Nani

CURRENT CLUB: Juventus

POSITION: LW

THE STATS

Height (cm):	**185**
Club appearances:	**850**
Club goals:	**638**
Club trophies:	**26**
International appearances:	**164**
International goals:	**99**
International trophies:	**1**
Ballon d'Ors:	**5**

★★★ **HERO RATING: 94** ★★★

GREATEST MOMENTS

1 6TH AUGUST 2003, SPORTING LISBON 3–1 MANCHESTER UNITED

This was the moment when Cristiano became a future star. Right-back John O'Shea will never forget this friendly match where a skinny young Sporting winger made a complete fool of him with his speed and skill. Cristiano was the star of the show and by the end of the game, he was a Manchester United player.

2 21ST MAY 2008, MANCHESTER UNITED 1–1 CHELSEA (6–5 ON PENALTIES)

Cristiano had already won the Premier League title but he was desperate to win the Champions League too. He scored an amazing header to give Manchester United the lead in the final against Chelsea. Cristiano missed a penalty in the shoot-out but his team still went on to win the Double.

3 16TH APRIL 2009, PORTO 0–1 MANCHESTER UNITED

Cristiano has scored loads of amazing goals but they don't get any better than this strike in the Champions League semi-final. From forty yards out, the ball flew like an arrow into the top corner. Thanks to Cristiano's wondergoal, Manchester United were through to another Champions League final.

4 24TH MAY 2014, REAL MADRID 4–1 ATLÉTICO MADRID

The Real Madrid fans had been waiting eleven years for 'La Décima', their tenth Champions League trophy. Cristiano's goals got them all the way to the 2014 final and his penalty in extra-time gave them the victory. He took off his shirt and roared like The Incredible Hulk.

5 10TH JULY 2016, PORTUGAL 1–0 FRANCE

After leading his country to the Euro 2016 final, Cristiano got injured early on against France. He was devastated to miss the biggest game of his life but from the bench, he cheered and coached his team to victory. At the final whistle, Cristiano was there to lift the trophy.

PLAY LIKE YOUR HEROES

THE CRISTIANO RONALDO GOAL CELEBRATION

STEP 1: Score an amazing goal.

STEP 2: Run towards the fans, smiling, nodding and pointing at yourself.

STEP 3: As you get towards the corner flag, jump into the air with your arms up high.

STEP 4: In mid-air, spin around so that you now have your back to the fans and they can all see the name and number on the back of your shirt.

STEP 5: As you land, keep your feet wide apart and bring your arms down dramatically until they are slightly behind your body.

STEP 6: Scream loudly with your mouth wide open in an 'O' shape.

STEP 7: Hold that pose until all of your team-mates run over and hug you.

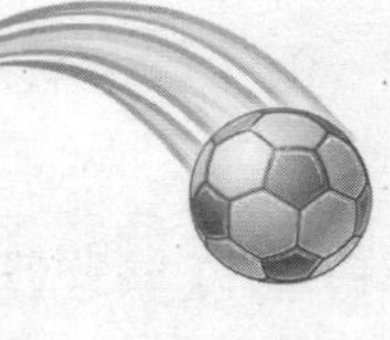

TEST YOUR KNOWLEDGE

QUESTIONS

1. Why did Dolores and Dinis choose the name 'Ronaldo' for their fourth child?

2. How old was Cristiano when he left Madeira and where did he go?

3. Who was Cristiano's biggest rival in the Sporting youth team?

4. How old was Cristiano when he made his first-team debut for Sporting Lisbon, and what shirt number did he wear?

5. Who was Sir Alex Ferguson looking to replace at Manchester United when he signed Cristiano?

6. Which Manchester United teammate did Cristiano clash with at the 2006 World Cup, and why?

7. Who was the Manchester United first-team coach who helped to make Cristiano an even better goalscorer?

8. How much did Real Madrid pay to sign Cristiano in 2009?

9. What shirt number did Cristiano wear when he first arrived at Real Madrid and why?

10. How many Champions League finals has Cristiano played in and how many goals has he scored?

11. How many major international tournaments has Cristiano played in for Portugal?

Answers below. . . No cheating!

1. Dolores liked the actor and President of the United States, Ronald Reagan. 2. He was 12 years old and he went to Lisbon. 3. Ricardo Quaresma. 4. He was 17 years old and he wore Number 28. 5. David Beckham. 6. Wayne Rooney. Cristiano helped to get him sent off when England played Portugal in the quarter-finals. 7. René Meulensteen. 8. £80 million. 9. He wore Number 9 because club legend Raúl already wore Number 7. 10. He has played in five finals (2008, 2009, 2014, 2016, 2017) and he has scored four goals, plus a penalty in the 2016 shoot-out. 11. Seven (Euro 2004, World Cup 2006, Euro 2008, World Cup 2010, Euro 2012, World Cup 2014, Euro 2016).

CAN'T GET ENOUGH OF ULTIMATE FOOTBALL HEROES?

Check out heroesfootball.com for quizzes, games, and competitions!

Plus join the Ultimate Football Heroes Fan Club to score exclusive content and be the first to hear about new books and events. heroesfootball.com/subscribe/